ARISE, TAKE THE YOUNG CHILD AND HIS MOTHER, AND FLEE INTO EGYPT

THE
BIBLE STORY BOOK
FOR BOYS AND GIRLS
by
JANE EAYRE FRYER
IN COLLABORATION WITH
REV. JOHN G. FRYER
ILLUSTRATED BY
EDWIN JOHN PRITTIE
THE JOHN C. WINSTON COMPANY
PHILADELPHIA, PA.

PRINTED IN THE U. S. A.

PREFACE

In writing this book the author's chief purpose has been to make the Bible real and vivid to the children of to-day by a sympathetic and reverent presentation of the principal Bible stories. The subject is presented from the child's point of view, because that method of approach (which is the method of the great Teacher himself) has proved so successful in the seven books of the Mary Frances Story Instruction Series. Nowhere has there been a conscious departure from the plain meaning of the Biblical narrative, or anything added not clearly contained therein. For the sake of vividness, some of the characters have been allowed to tell their own stories in the first person.

It seems hardly necessary to say that the author regards instruction in Bible truth as the precious birthright of every child, which it is a primary duty of parent and teacher to see that he receives.

JANE EAYRE FRYER.

MERCHANTVILLE, N. J.

CONTENTS

SPREADING THE GOOD TIDINGS

ILLUSTRATIONS

BEFORE
THE
FLOOD

BEFORE THE FLOOD

"In the beginning God created the heaven and the earth."

—GENESIS 1:1.

WRITING A BOOK IN OLDEN TIMES

I

MAKING FRIENDS WITH THE BIBLE PEOPLE

IF you had been watching, one early winter morning, the big old country house in which Aunt Maria lived, you would have known that something unusual was about to happen. For the twentieth time that morning, the little old lady opened the big colonial front door and stepped out.

Shading her eyes with her hand, she peered up the road, and for the twentieth time she exclaimed, "No sign of them yet! Such heathen contraptions!"

And if you had followed her into the house, you would have heard her mutter to herself: "What's the world coming to, anyway? Such contraptions! I'd never have trusted the best driver that ever drove an automobile to bring those precious children."

The "precious children" she was so eagerly expecting were Billy and Mary Frances, who were coming to visit their great aunt while their parents were away on a winter trip to Europe.

Then you would have seen her peer out the window, and heard her mutter again: "No sign of them yet! My, I'm thankful

I didn't invent such dangerous machines! Why, what's that noise? I do believe a car has stopped in front of the house!"

She hurried to the door, but almost before she turned the knob, it flew open and the two children came running in.

Mary Frances flung her arms around the little old lady's neck. "Aunt Maria, were you worried? Did you think we had had an accident?" she exclaimed breathlessly.

"We had two blow-outs," Billy stated, rather proudly.

"Blow-outs!" repeated the old lady, who did not understand what he meant. "Was anyone killed, child?"

"Oh, no, that means the air went out of the tires," the boy explained.

"Well, I am certainly thankful to see you safe and sound," said the old lady rather stiffly, as though a little ashamed of having shown that she had not understood. "Let us go thank your friends for bringing you, and invite them in."

But their friends could not be persuaded to stop; and so, bidding the children and their aunt good-by, they drove away.

It was Saturday afternoon. Mary Frances stood looking out of the window with her face pressed against the pane. All day the snow had been falling, and the wind had been blowing it in high piles against the buildings in her aunt's garden. Her brother was having a good time, bravely trying to shovel a path through the thick whiteness.

"Oh, dear!" she sighed to herself, as she watched him; "Oh, dear, how I hope it stops snowing before morning! I'm afraid Aunt Maria will make us learn a whole long chapter of the Bible if we cannot get to Sunday school."

Just at that moment the old lady came into the room.

"What are you doing, child?" she asked. "Come over to the fire. Bring your chair."

Mary Frances brought the little old-fashioned chair, and sat down opposite her aunt, in front of the blazing logs.

"Do you think the storm will keep us from Sunday school?" she asked.

"I cannot say, child," said her aunt; "but if it does, we can have Sunday school at home."

"Oh, dear!" thought Mary Frances. "Oh, dear, now I feel sure we'll have to learn those chapters, just as father did when he was a boy and lived with Aunt Maria."

But she said aloud, "Aunt Maria, won't you please tell me a story?"

"Child, do you know the Bible story of the beginning of the world?" asked the old lady instantly, as though she had been expecting this request.

"No," said Mary Frances, drawing her chair closer to her aunt's. "Please—will you tell it to me?"

"I cannot tell such a wonderful thing in my own words, but I will read it to you," she replied. "I suspect that you do not know many of the stories in the Bible. Mary Frances, I believe it's an act of Providence that you children have been sent to visit me while your parents are away. It will be no fault of mine if you do not learn some of the most beautiful stories ever told to human beings."

"Stories!" exclaimed Mary Frances in delight. "You will tell us stories, Aunt Maria?"

"I want you to read some of them yourselves, and then tell them to me," replied her aunt. "To-morrow we will begin, for I hardly think we shall be able to go far through the snow."

Just then Billy came bounding in. "Ready for tea?" asked Aunt Maria, in answer to his smile, and taking Mary Frances' hand, she led the way into the dining room.

"Fine," said the hungry boy, between bites, as they told him of their plan.

Aunt Maria's prophecy came true. When Mary Frances woke up the next morning, the snow was still falling. No fences were to be seen, and there was no sign of life out of doors, except a few snowbirds which were gathered on the step outside the dining-room door, busily eating the crumbs which Billy, who was also an early bird, had already thrown out to them.

"Sunday school at home," whispered Mary Frances, fastening her shoe laces. "I must hurry, or I shall be late to breakfast."

"Good morning, Aunt Maria," she said, entering the dining room. "I saw the birds eating their breakfast. I should love to feed them to-morrow."

"So you shall, child," answered her aunt, with a smile. "You look very happy this morning."

"I am thinking about the stories—the stories you said we must hear," replied Mary Frances.

Right after breakfast Aunt Maria said, "Now we will have our Sunday school. For our lesson I will read you the story of The Beginning of the World."

And so the children heard about the beginning of things, as told in the first and a part of the second chapter of Genesis.

So God Banished Adam from the Garden, and Hand in Hand Eve Went with Him

II

THE BEAUTIFUL GARDEN

THAT afternoon, Mary Frances was sitting by the fire, feeling very lonely as she thought of her father and mother, who would soon be far away, and her brother was lying on the floor, idly poking the blazing logs, when Aunt Maria came quietly into the room, carrying a mysterious-looking book.

"I have a surprise for you, Billy—an old book I had forgotten all about," she said, dusting it off carefully, and placing it in his hands.

As soon as the boy felt the soft brown leather covers, and glanced curiously inside, he knew that this book was not like other books. For one thing, the pages, which were yellow with age, were not printed; they were written in a fine long running hand, a bit faded, but still quite easy to read.

"Oh, Aunty, what clear writing!" he exclaimed.

"Yes, child, that is the handwriting of my brother, your Uncle Ben—really your great-uncle, you know, who was pastor of our church when he was a young man. He was very fond of telling Bible stories. Sometimes it seemed just as if the Bible people were present and really talking. He wrote down many of his stories in this old book."

"Oh, I should love to read them!" cried Mary Frances.

"Of course you would," said the boy; "but this is my book," holding it tight; "Aunt Maria gave it to me." The old lady looked on amused, and Billy relented. "Well, I'll let you read it," he said, "if you'll read it aloud to me." "Yes, that's a good plan, Mary Frances," said Aunt Maria. "Suppose you read the first story, and tell me about it afterwards."

As Aunt Maria left the room, Mary Frances turned to the first story in Uncle Ben's book, and began to read aloud.

* * * * * * *

The Story of the Beautiful Garden

When God had made the earth, and covered it with grass and trees, and put birds in the air, and fish in the sea, and animals on the land, he chose the most beautiful spot in it for the home of man.

This spot was a wonderful garden called the Garden of Eden, and in it he put the man he had made. This man was called Adam, and he was there alone. His duty was to care for the garden and keep it in order.

The most beautiful trees in the world grew in the garden, and a river of sparkling water flowed through it to water them. The trees were very pleasant, and their fruit was good for food. In the center of the garden there grew the tree of the knowledge of good and evil. It was a marvelous tree, and so God gave the keeper of the garden strict commands concerning it.

"You may eat the fruit of every tree in the garden except one," God told him; "and that one is the tree of the knowledge of good and evil. You must not eat of that, for in the day that you do you will surely die."

Of course, Adam, who was the keeper, obeyed, and thought little more about it, apparently. What troubled him most was that he was lonely. When God saw this, he said, "It is not good for man to be alone; I will give him company."

So God brought the animals that he had created, and all the birds of the air to Adam and told him to name them. He named every bird that flies and every animal in the garden, and he had a very happy time while doing it. At last all were named—but Adam was still lonely.

God saw this and caused him to fall into a deep sleep; while he was asleep, God took one of the man's ribs from his side, and formed a woman, and brought her to the man, and she became his wife.

For a long time they lived happily together in their beautiful home, with the birds and animals about them. They loved each other and all created things; they talked with God as a friend, and he talked with them, and they knew nothing of evil or wrong.

Now, among the animals in the garden there was one they cared the least about; this was the serpent.

One day the woman was very restless and wanted something to interest her. The serpent, who was watching, always watching, asked, "Has God told you not to eat the fruit of any particular tree in the garden?"

"Yes," she replied, without thinking, "we may eat the fruit of all the trees except one, the great tree in the center of the garden. God has warned us that we must not eat of it lest we die."

This was what Adam had often told her, and she repeated it without thinking.

When the serpent heard this, he said, "That cannot be; you shall not surely die, for God well knows that on the day you eat of it your eyes will be opened, and you will be like gods, knowing good and evil."

Like the foolish woman that she was, she believed the tempter. Having nothing better to do, she thought there would be no harm in looking at the tree, at any rate. So off she went. Now, on this day the fruit happened to be just ripe, and a delight to the eye. How tempting it was! As she looked at it, she wondered if it would really make one wise, and then—she reached up and plucked some of the ripest.

She held it in her hand and admired it. How good it looked and smelled! Then she put some in her mouth. How good it tasted! It was better than all the other fruit of the garden. Off she tripped to her husband and offered some to him, and he ate, too.

Even while they were eating, the sky overhead suddenly grew dark; they looked at each other and knew they had done wrong. The only thing they were forbidden to do they had done. For the first time, they were ashamed, and tried to hide. They took great leaves and fastened them together, and tried to cover themselves, for they were shivering with fear. But nothing further happened all that afternoon.

When the evening came they heard the voice of God, who was walking in the garden, and they hid among the thick trees, and tried to conceal themselves from his presence.

"Where are you?" It was the voice of God calling Adam.

"I heard a voice in the garden," he answered, timidly; "and I was afraid and hid myself, because I was not clothed."

"Who told you that you were not clothed?" said the voice again. "Have you eaten the fruit of the tree which I commanded you not to eat?"

"The woman you gave me offered me the fruit and I ate," he replied.

"What is this you have done?" the voice asked the woman, sternly.

"The serpent tempted me and I ate," she replied, frightened.

At this the serpent, who was listening, tried to sneak away, but the stern voice overtook him and stopped him to hear his sentence.

"Because you have done this thing," God said, "you are

cursed above all cattle and above every beast of the field; you shall crawl upon the ground and eat dust all the days of your life, and the children of the woman shall hate the serpent, and shall bruise its head, and the serpent shall bruise their heels."

To the woman God said: "Because you have done this, I will greatly increase your suffering, and your children shall cause you sorrow, and your husband shall rule over you."

To Adam he said: "Because you have disobeyed my command and eaten of the fruit which I commanded you not to eat, the ground is cursed for your sake; by labor you shall eat of it all the days of your life; it shall bring forth thorns and thistles, and you shall eat the plants of the field; in the sweat of your face you shall eat bread, until you return to the ground from which you were taken, for dust you are and to dust you shall return."

When the voice stopped speaking they looked at each other sorrowfully. Then Adam called his wife "Eve," because she was to be the mother of all living. After that they wore clothing of skins which God had made for them, and were a little comforted.

But their first happiness was never to return, for one day God said: "See, the man is become like one of us, knowing good and evil; I must banish him from the garden, lest he put forth his hand and take the fruit of the tree of life, and eat, and live for ever."

So God banished Adam from the Garden of Eden, to till the ground out of which he was taken, and hand in hand Eve went with him. How frightened they were! When they were outside they turned and looked back, and there they saw angels standing at the gate, and a flaming sword which turned every way, guarding the path to the tree of life.

AND LO, TOWARD EVENING SHE FLEW BACK WITH AN OLIVE LEAF IN HER MOUTH

III

NOAH, THE SHIP-BUILDER

"AUNT MARIA, what happened to Adam and Eve after that?" asked Mary Frances in the evening, as the three were seated comfortably before the fire. She had just finished telling her aunt the Garden of Eden story.

"What happened after that?" repeated the old lady. "My child, it's a sad story, one of the saddest in the Book. You can read it for yourself in the fourth chapter of Genesis."

"No, Aunt Maria, if it's sad, please let's read it together!"

So the old lady put on her glasses and read, in her old-fashioned way, the tale of two brothers—how the older killed the younger, and what came of it.

Mary Frances listened without a word till the end. Then she cried, "Poor Abel! What made Cain kill him?"

The old lady shook her head. "That's a hard question, dear," she said, sadly. "Perhaps he was jealous."

All sat silent for a while, looking into the fire. At length the little girl asked, "What happened after that, Aunt Maria?"

"Well, the earth became more and more thickly populated, people grew worse and worse as hundreds of years rolled by—and then came Noah."

"Noah!" cried Billy. "Father has often told me about him."

"I don't doubt it. That was one of your Uncle Ben's favorite stories. Your father loved to hear him tell it, just as if Noah were telling it himself to his grandchildren. It is told in the sixth, seventh, and eighth chapters of Genesis; and also in Uncle Ben's book. Suppose you read Uncle Ben's account this evening, and tell me about it to-morrow."

"Yes, it's your turn to read now, Mister Billy," said Mary Frances, laughingly.

So the brother and sister settled in a quiet corner under the lamp, found the place in the old leather covered book, and were soon lost in the story of Noah. As they read on, it seemed almost as if Noah himself were talking.

* * * * * * *

The Building of the Ark

When I started to build a ship on dry land, far away from the sea, people opened their eyes in wonder. Such a thing had never been heard of since the world began. They tapped their heads and said, "Noah has gone mad!"

But as the thing turned out, I was wise and they were foolish. This they learned when it was too late.

God had talked with me one day. This was not strange, for I walked with God and always tried to do his will.

"Noah," God said to me, "men have become violent and desperately wicked; they quarrel continually and seek to do evil. There is no good in them. Their time has come; I am about to destroy them from off the face of the earth."

I listened in fear and wonder, but what could I say? I knew that what God said was true, for I had tried to warn them, but they only laughed and paid no heed to my warnings.

Then the Lord told me to do a strange thing—to build a ship on dry land, where no water was; and I obeyed, for who was I to question his command?

"Build an ark of gopher wood," he directed; "and cover it with pitch inside and out, so that it shall be water-tight. Make it three hundred cubits long, fifty cubits wide, and thirty cubits high,* with windows in it and a door in the side, and lower, second, and third stories."

God explained further what he was about to do.

"Behold," he said, "I will bring a flood of waters upon the earth, to destroy everything that breathes from under heaven; only you and your family and the animals which you gather shall be left alive. For when the flood comes, you and your family shall enter the ark and be saved."

I thanked God for his mercy, and began to carry out his orders. I went to my wife and told her all that God had said. Then I went into the forest with my three sons, and cut down great trees and made them into planks, and brought them into the broad field before my house.

Now the wood of the gopher tree is light and very strong, and with it we laid the keel of the ship in the field, according to the plan which God had given me. My neighbors gathered about and watched us curiously, and asked, "Noah, what are you trying to do?"

"God is about to destroy both man and beast by flood,"

---

* Allowing 21 inches for a cubit, the ark would be 525 feet in length, 87 feet 6 inches in width, and 52 feet 6 inches in height.

I replied; "and I am building this ark to save my family. Repent, and perhaps God will turn aside his anger."

They went away and laughed, and said, "The earth always has been and always will be." Behind my back they called me an old fool, although they dared not call me so to my face.

Year after year went by, and slowly plank by plank the ark grew, the lower story, the second story, the third story; and then we put on the roof and made the door. Up near the roof we left a window which ran all around the ark. After that we built rooms inside for my family, stalls for the animals, and nests for the birds, and made great storage places for food for man and beast, just as God had said.

Day by day the people came from far and near to watch us, and day by day their wonder grew. Day by day I warned them to repent, for the day of doom drew nearer and nearer; but still they scoffed and mocked and would not listen.

The Loading of the Ark

At last the ark was finished. There it stood in the broad field, a great floating house. And the people came and wondered, and said, "Where is the water to float it? What a joke!"

Then I began to gather into the field the animals that were to go with us in the ark. Of clean animals, such as the sheep and the cow, I took seven pairs of each; and of unclean, such as the lion and the tiger, I took one pair of each, of the things that creep upon the ground, one pair of each; and of the birds of the air, seven pairs of each.

When the people saw the animals assembled in the great field about the ark, their amazement knew no bounds.

"Was ever such a thing heard of?" they cried. "The old man has gone mad, and his sons with him!"

But I was so sorry for them that I went among them and warned them again and again to repent and turn from their folly and wickedness, but they would not heed and cried out that the folly and wickedness was mine. They brought their heathen priests to reason with me, but the priests were worse than their people—the blind leading the blind to destruction.

At last all was ready; the ark was finished, the beasts and birds were gathered, and food for all was stored. As God had commanded me, so I had done.

Then, as I lay awake in the night, God spoke to me and said, "Noah."

"Here am I, Lord," I replied.

"You only have I seen righteous in all the earth. Come, you and yours, into the ark. For after seven days I will cause it to rain forty days and forty nights; and every living thing will I destroy from off the face of the earth."

I slept no more, but lay all night trembling to think of the terror of the foolish people when my words should come true; but who was I, to question the wisdom of the Creator?

As soon as the morning was light, I called my sons and told them of God's command. Then we began to load the ship. All day long the animals passed into the ark. Two by two, male and female, side by side they walked, as if they knew their safety hung upon it. Even the wild brutes were tame and obedient to our word. The elephant, the lion, the tiger, the leopard, the camel, the cow, the sheep, the deer, the antelope, all went in and took their places in the stalls provided for them; and the smaller brutes and creeping things passed into their holes and dens. Then the birds, which were flying about in the sun, came at our call, and sweeping low, flew in at the door, two by two, and took their places in their nests.

For seven days we loaded the ship, and all the while the sun shone, the earth was dry, and there was no sign of rain. All the while the doomed people stood about, watching us. Some grew angry and called us vile names, and others mocked, but none would believe. And still we worked, unmindful of their anger and their mirth, until on the seventh day we placed our families in their cabins, and all was done.

Then, as the sun was going down, my three sons went aboard. I walked around the ship for the last time, and examined it as a good captain should, to see that all was safe and right. All was done as God had commanded.

The time had now come. I saw that the sky was growing black and the wind was rising. I pointed up, but the crowd only laughed, and one cried, "It's only a shower!" Their taunts and jeers followed me as I went aboard, and I wept for very sorrow to think what was about to come upon them. The moment I stepped inside, the door was closed by unseen hands. The Lord had shut us in.

The Coming of the Flood

As the darkness fell, we sat awed and silent, awaiting what should come. Then the rain began to beat upon the roof, and the wind arose and struck the ark with such a mighty blast that she rocked upon her keel. But we were not afraid; we knew that we were safe in the hand that had planned our refuge.

The storm grew apace; the thunders roared, and the lightnings flashed and lit up all the ark with an unearthly light. The beasts called to each other from their stalls, and the birds fluttered in their nests; but neither beast nor bird was frightened, for they knew they were safe from the wrath of the storm.

Then the windows of heaven were opened, and the waters fell in sheets and torrents and floods, so that it seemed as if the roof of the ark must be beaten in—but it held fast. The fountains of the great deep were broken up, and the waters came rolling in from the sea across the land. We felt the waves flowing fast under our keel—and then the ark quivered and lifted. Slowly and evenly she rose upon the waters and floated like a thing of life.

"Truly," I said, "the hand of God is upon the earth."

I thought of the terror of those who had mocked God. Now

they were praying for safety, when it was too late. As I peered through the darkness, I thought I could almost see them climbing to the tops of their houses as they rocked upon their foundations, then tottered and fell; climbing the trees, the hills, the mountains, as the fatal waters rose up and up their sides after them—until I could bear the thought no longer, and I prayed for their souls.

Then a quietness came upon me; and I took a light and examined the roof, and went down into the lower stories to see if the bottom was safe. The inside was as dry as the palm of my hand. There was no drop of moisture anywhere. Our gallant ship held tight and strong. I spoke to the beasts in their stalls as they munched their food. Even the wildest looked at me with friendly eyes as I comforted them. After this, I returned to my family, and we sat and talked.

Lest men should forget, I marked the date of our entering the ark. It was in the six hundredth year of my life, in the second month, on the seventeenth day of the month, that the great deluge began. For forty days and forty nights, as God had said, the rain descended and the waters rose higher and higher upon the earth, until all the hills and the high mountains were covered, and every living thing upon the earth, both man and beast, perished. Only the fish in the sea remained alive.

Day by day we fed the beasts and birds their appointed food, which we had stored for them, so that none suffered from hunger; day by day the rain kept on falling.

So forty days passed, and on the fortieth day God sent a great wind to blow over the earth; the windows of heaven were stopped and the rain was over, but the waters covered the earth for yet another hundred and fifty days.

The Going Down of the Waters

Then slowly but surely the waters began to sink. Meanwhile, the ark floated wherever the waters carried it, for it was without sail or rudder; and in the seventh month, on the seventeenth day of the month it rested on the highest mountains of that country—the mountains of Ar-a-rat. How glad we were to feel the ark safe on solid ground once more!

The waters kept going down by degrees until the first day of the tenth month, and on that day the tops of the neighboring mountains began to be seen.

I waited forty days longer, and then opened a window and sent forth a raven; the raven flew to and fro for a time, and then sped away and did not return.

Then I sent forth another messenger, a dove; she flew about and, finding no rest for the sole of her foot, came back frightened to the window. I reached out my hand and took her into the ark, and glad enough she was to fly back to her old nest.

After waiting seven days longer I sent the dove out again, and lo, toward evening she flew back with an olive leaf in her mouth. So I knew that the waters were abated from off the earth.

I waited another seven days and sent out the dove once more, and this time she did not return. So we removed the covering from the ark and looked out, and saw that the ground was dry.

Even then we waited for God's command, and it was eight weeks before God spoke to me and said, "Come out of the ark, you and your wife, and your sons and their wives, and bring every living thing with you."

So we all disembarked from our floating home, on which we had lived for more than a year. After all were safely landed, my first act was to build an altar, and offer a burnt offering.

The offering was very pleasing to the Lord, and he said:

"I will not curse the ground any more for man's sake; neither will I again destroy every living thing as I have done. While the earth remains, seedtime and harvest, and cold and heat, and summer and winter, and day and night shall not cease."

We bowed ourselves to the ground before the Lord, as he went on speaking:

"I will set my rainbow in the cloud, as a sign. When you see a cloud, and the rainbow in the cloud, you may know that I remember my promise that the waters shall no more become a flood to destroy the earth."

Whenever we saw the beautiful arch span the sky after a storm, we knew that God was keeping his promise.

* * * * * * *

The brother and sister read to the end, and wished the story had been longer. Soon after, they took their lamps, kissed their aunt good-night, and went upstairs to bed. Billy fell asleep and dreamed that great waves of water were rolling under his bed; in the morning he awoke with a start—but there were no waves. Only the wind was whistling about the gables of the old house, and through the window he saw the sun shining brightly on a white blanket of snow.

THE CHOSEN PEOPLE

THE CHOSEN PEOPLE

"I will make of thee a great nation . . . and in thee shall all families of the earth be blessed."—GENESIS 12 : 2, 3.

"LET ME, I PRAY YOU, DRINK A LITTLE WATER FROM YOUR PITCHER"

IV

THE CHOSEN FAMILY

THE next evening when the children finished telling their aunt what they had learned about Noah the ship-builder, the old lady sat quiet for several minutes. At length she spoke.

"Children," she said, "you amaze me with the way you tell these Bible stories. Not only do you know the order of events, but you make the people so real that they seem to live. While you were talking, I could see, in my mind's eye, a picture of what happened, better than I ever saw it before—and I have told that story over and over again."

The old lady went on, "Keep all of these stories in mind, and read them again and again; and some day, when you are grown, tell them to children. You make the people of ages past seem to live in the present; and that is a wonderful gift.

"Why, I could almost hear the builders working on that

ship," she continued; "and I could almost see the animals and birds taking their places when it was ready."

The children hardly knew what reply to make to such praise, so Mary Frances asked what story they should read next.

"The story of the man who left his home at God's command, and went into a far country," replied her aunt.

"Oh, Aunty, won't you tell us that one?" asked Mary Frances.

Much pleased, the old lady began the story of Abram.

* * * * * * *

Abram, the Friend of God

To be called "The Friend of God" is a very great honor. There is only one greater title—but that is a story to be told later. This title did not come to A-bram easily; he won it only after many strange and dangerous adventures.

Abram was a true child of the out-of-doors, born in the tent of his father, Te-rah, a wandering shepherd chief. The land of his birth was a land of idols in southern Asia, where the great river Eu-phra-tes flows into the Persian Gulf. The people of that land bowed down to rude images of brass and wood and stone. Some of them even worshiped the moon.

Abram looked at the people about him worshiping their foolish idols, sometimes even making human sacrifices, and he said to himself, "Come what will, I will never worship them." And he never did.

One day, after he was grown up, his father said, "I have heard of a wonderful land on the other side of the Great Desert, where there are green pastures and plenty of water for our flocks; let us seek it."

Now this desert was the Arabian Desert, which they could not cross with their cattle, because its sands were hot and dry. The only way to reach the other side was to go around it.

Striking their tents, and driving their flocks and herds before them, they set out on their long and dangerous journey. They wandered slowly along the banks of the great river, until at last they came to the hill country in the north where the river rises, and there they pitched their tents at a place called Haran. With Abram and his father were Abram's beautiful young wife Sarai, and his nephew, Lot, who accompanied him to Canaan.

But Abram's father was never to see the land of Canaan. While they were encamped at Haran, the brave old man died, at the age of two hundred and five, and his son became chief in his place. Abram was now seventy-five years old, still a young man for those days.

God's Promise

Soon after his father's death came the great event of Abram's life—God spoke to him. He lay one night sleepless in his tent, his mind troubled and full of foreboding, thinking of his father and his distant home, when he heard a voice. Such a voice he had never heard before, but he recognized it. It was the voice he had so often wished to hear, so he was not afraid.

"Abram," the voice called.

"Here am I, Lord," he answered.

"Go out from this country, leave your people and the land of your fathers, and go to a land that I will show you."

Such was the startling message.

"I will make of your family a great nation," the voice went on; "and I will bless you and make your name great; you shall be a blessing to others, and through you all the families of the earth shall be blessed."

At last Abram's trust was rewarded; his fear vanished. Now he knew there was one true God, for had not God spoken to him?

He lost no time in setting out on his great adventure. He quickly broke up his camp, struck his tents, gathered his flocks and herds, and went forth, not knowing where he was going.

He was on his way to the Promised Land, but he did not

know that. He only knew that God would guide him, and that was enough.

The great caravan headed by Abram and Lot first traveled west and then south, slowly, because of the cattle. After a time they came to a place called Shechem, and encamped under a great oak tree. There were wild Arab tribes about who looked at them curiously, but did not molest them.

Here the Lord appeared to Abram a second time, and said, "Unto your children will I give this land."

So the land was called the Promised Land, because God promised it to Abram and his children after him. There he built an altar under the oak tree, and worshiped the true God who had appeared to him.

Abram never doubted God's word, and when he was ninety-nine years old, the Lord appeared to him again.

Abram was overcome, and fell on his face. And God talked with him, and comforted him, saying, "You shall be the father of a multitude of nations. Neither shall your name any more be called Abram, but your name shall be A-bra-ham; for the father of a multitude of nations have I made you. As for Sarai your wife, you shall not call her name Sarai, but Sarah shall be her name. And I will bless her, and she shall have a son, and she shall be a mother of nations."

The Offering of Isaac

Soon after this event, Abraham and Sarah moved from Hebron, and pitched their tents at Gerar, and there Isaac their son was born, as God had promised.

Isaac grew up to young manhood, an obedient, gentle lad devoted to his father and mother. His education was that of a young chief, living in the open. Of books there were none, but in the care of flocks and herds he became an expert. In the quiet evening he sat in the tent door with his parents, and listened to the thrilling tales his father told of his travels and adventures since leaving his early home in far-off Babylonia.

Then one day came the great test of Abraham's life, which was to prove for all time that the old chief was rightly named "The Friend of God."

In the night he heard the voice of which he was no longer afraid, and which he loved so well, the voice of his Great Friend.

"Abraham," came the call.

"Here am I, Lord," he answered.

Then came the most startling command that had ever been given to man, a command that even Abraham could not understand, so hard was the task it set him.

"Take now your son," the voice said, "your only son, whom you love, even Isaac, and go up into the land of Mo-ri-ah, and offer him there for a burnt offering upon one of the mountains which I will show you."

Abraham would willingly have sacrificed his own life for his son—but Isaac! He did not understand. All night long he tossed upon his couch; and then he remembered his own words to his Great Friend, "Shall not the Judge of all the earth do right?" And he said, "He will do right; I must obey."

At the morning light the loyal old chief arose, and saddled his beast; called two of his young men to accompany him, and Isaac, his son. He cut the wood for the burnt offering, took provisions for the journey, and set out for the place of which God had told him. He did not—he dared not—tell Sarah his errand.

Over the hills they went, and on the third day they saw the mountains afar off, and soon arrived at the foot of Mount Moriah.

"Remain here with the beast, and I and the lad will go up into the mountain to worship, and come again to you," Abraham said to the two young men.

He had scarcely slept for worry on the journey, and yet there kept ringing in his ears the question, "Shall not the Judge of all the earth do right?" and the comforting answer came as often as the question, "He is my Friend. He cannot do wrong."

Abraham took the wood for the burnt offering, and laid it upon Isaac; and he took in his hand the fire he had prepared, and the knife; and they went side by side up the mountain.

"Father!" said Isaac.

Abraham was so startled at the word that he almost dropped the fire.

"Here am I, my son," he said.

"Father," said Isaac, "see, here is the wood and the fire, but where is the lamb for the burnt offering?"

Abraham had said nothing to Isaac of what he was about to do.

"God himself will provide a lamb for the burnt offering, my son," was all the reply he could make.

So they climbed slowly, until they came to the place that God had pointed out.

There Abraham built the altar, and laid the wood in order upon it—moving like a man in a dream, while Isaac stood silently by, watching him. The old chief looked about him, but there was no sign.

He waited a minute longer, but still there was no sign. With the tears running down his face, he threw his arms about the lad, and told him gently what he was commanded to do. Isaac was startled—who would not be?—but he did not resist. He had never learned how to disobey; his father's word was law.

The old man bound him gently as he lay upon the altar. Then he bent over and kissed him, and his tears fell upon Isaac's face. Then he stretched out his hand, and picked up the knife to slay his son.

He was about to lift the knife, when—

"Abraham! Abraham!" Quick and sharp the words were spoken. It was the voice of the Angel of the Lord calling to him.

"Here am I," Abraham cried, in sudden hope.

"Lay not your hand upon the lad, neither do anything to

"Lay Not Your Hand Upon the Lad"

him: for now I know that you fear God, seeing that you have not withheld your son, your only son, from me."

Then in a frenzy of joy, Abraham cut with the hated knife the thongs that bound Isaac, and lifting him up, embraced him, this time with tears of relief and happiness.

After a moment he heard a noise behind him, and there in the thicket he saw a ram caught by his horns. Abraham quickly caught the ram, and offered him up for a burnt offering in the place of his son.

"The name of this place shall be Jehovah-jireh," (Jehovah will provide) Abraham cried.

Now for the second time, the Angel of the Lord called to Abraham out of heaven, and said, "By myself have I sworn, says the Lord, because you have done this thing, and have not withheld your son, your only son: that in blessing I will bless you, and in multiplying I will multiply your people as the stars of heaven, and as the sand which is upon the sea shore; and your people shall possess the gate of their enemies; and in them shall all the nations of the earth be blessed; because you have obeyed my voice."

Thus the friendship of Abraham with God was sealed forever. Together father and son went happily down the mountain, and returned to the young men, and they packed up and went home to Gerar.

But, so far as the story goes, Abraham never told Sarah, nor did Isaac ever tell his mother, what happened on the top of Mount Moriah.

* * * * * * *

"You have become so interested in the story of this boy Isaac, my dear children," added the old lady, "that I want you to learn his love story. After you have read it in the twenty-fourth chapter of Genesis, you may read it in Uncle Ben's book. Abraham was afraid to let Isaac, who was his only son, go on a long journey to find a wife, so he sent his steward instead. Uncle

Ben lets the steward tell how he found Rebekah. Suppose you read it together and tell me about it to-morrow."

This is the steward's story, as Mary Frances read it aloud from the quaint old book.

The Courtship of Isaac and Rebekah

When Isaac's mother, Sarah, died in her tent under the great oaks at Hebron, she had lived one hundred twenty-seven years. The old chief and his son buried her in the cave of Mach-pe-lah, a beautiful shaded spot near by.

After that, the two men were very lonely, and drew nearer to each other in their grief. Sarah was a very lovely woman, famous for her beauty, which she never lost, even in old age. Isaac was her only child; they were devoted to each other, and she could hardly bear him out of her sight. When not busy with his father's great flocks and herds, he was her constant companion, and always lived in her tent.

Father and son often sat together in their tent door in the long evenings and talked over the future.

"I came to this land as a stranger, and I am still a stranger," the old man would say. "I have grown very rich in cattle and gold and silver, and it will all be yours when I am gone."

"I hope you will live a long time yet, father," Isaac would reply.

"No, my son, I cannot live long. You must seek a wife, but she cannot be from the heathen tribes round about us. Your mother and I left the far-off land of our birth to escape idolatry, and to seek the true God, and here we found him. He is your God, too."

Thus they talked evening after evening, and so the time went by.

Then one day the caravan of an Arab chief on his way from the North to Egypt halted at their tent door, and Abraham, according to his custom, invited him to lodge for the night, and gave him water from his well and food for his camels.

Now the Arab chief had come through Pad-an-A-ram, Abraham's former home, and he told him the news of his family, and mentioned a daughter of the house, a beautiful girl, whom he had seen there. That was enough for Isaac; he could scarcely wait until the caravan had gone on its journey.

"Father," he said the next day, "let me go to see her."

His father understood, for he had been thinking the same thought.

"No, my son, that cannot be," and the old man shook his head. "You cannot leave this land which God has promised us. The journey is long and perilous, and harm might befall you, and I might die while you were away."

For the first time in his life, Isaac was tempted to rebel, but he waited.

"Son," said his father, "you are all I have. You must stay with me; there is nothing to do but to send a messenger."

So the old chief, who was a man of action, called me, his chief steward and oldest servant, into council. I often sat with them of an evening, and already I had guessed what was coming.

"Put your hand under my thigh, I pray you," he bade me.

This was the quaint way of taking an oath in those days.

"Now swear by the Lord, the God of heaven and earth," said the old chief solemnly to me, "that you will not seek a wife for my son from the daughters of the heathen among whom we dwell, but that you will go to my country, and to my people, and seek a wife for my son Isaac."

"Perhaps the woman will not be willing to come with me," I objected. "Shall I not then take your son to the land from which you came?"

"No," said Abraham, sternly, "you shall not take my son there. The Lord, the God of heaven, who took me from my father's house, and from the land of my birth, and who spoke to me, and swore to me, saying, 'To your son will I give this land,' he will send his angel before you, and you shall take a wife for my son from thence. If the woman be not willing to follow you, then you shall be free from your oath; only you must not take my son there."

Then I put my hand under the thigh of my master, and swore to do as he bade me.

Without loss of time, Isaac and I went among the camels and chose the finest of the herd to form the caravan. Then I selected the best drivers to accompany me, and there was a great stir in the camp. At last all was ready. Isaac decked the camels in their gay trappings, gave me beautiful jewelry from his mother's store, and costly gifts for the maiden's family; and the caravan set off on its happy adventure. Isaac accompanied it part way, and gave me secret instructions. I laughed, and nodded that I understood, while Isaac stood alone in the fields and longingly watched the brave array until the last camel was out of sight.

Then he returned to his tent to wait; for, with the utmost speed, it would be several weeks before we could return from Padan-Aram.

Day by day the caravan sped north by the old trail over which Abraham had driven his cattle more than sixty years before, and came at last to Padan-Aram, the city of Na-hor. It was evening when we reached the well outside the city, about the time when the women came to draw water.

I made the camels kneel down, and waited to see what would happen. Then, becoming anxious for the success of my delicate errand, I bowed my head and prayed.

"O Lord, the God of my master Abraham," I prayed, "send me good speed to-day, and show kindness to my master Abraham. Behold, I stand by the fountain of water; and the daughters of the city come out to draw water; and let it come to pass, that the maid to whom I shall say, 'Let down your pitcher, I pray you, that I may drink,' and she shall say, 'Drink, and I will give your camels drink also': let the same be the maid chosen for my master Isaac."

As I opened my eyes, almost before I had done speaking, I saw a young girl coming toward me, who was very fair to look upon.

I watched her respectfully as she went to the well, filled her pitcher, and put it on her shoulder. Then I ran to her, and said, "Let me, I pray you, drink a little water from your pitcher."

"Drink, my lord," she said, quickly lifting down her pitcher upon her hand and holding it for me to drink.

"I will draw for your camels also, until they have done drinking," she added.

Now it is no small task to water ten thirsty camels, but she hasted and emptied her pitcher into the trough, and ran to the well and drew, and poured the water into the trough for all the camels as their drivers led them up.

I stood by silently looking on, wondering whether the Lord had made my journey prosperous or not.

When the camels had done drinking, I took from my saddlebags a golden ring and two golden bracelets, and said, "Whose daughter are you? Tell me, I pray, is there room in your father's house to lodge us?"

She smiled at me, and I thought I had never seen so sweet a smile.

"I am the daughter of Beth-u-el," she replied, "My grandmother was Mil-cah, and my grandfather, Na-hor." Then she added, "We have both straw and food enough, and there is room to lodge in."

Then I gave her the ring and bracelets; and bowed my head and worshiped the Lord.

"Blessed be the Lord, the God of my master Abraham," I said, "who has not forsaken his mercy and his truth toward my master."

Then Re-bek-ah, for that was the girl's name, left her pitcher, and ran home and told her mother what I had said, and showed her the ring and the bracelets.

Now Rebekah had a brother whose name was La-ban; and when Laban heard, he ran out to me where I stood by the camels at the well.

"Come in, blessed of the Lord," he said. "Why do you stand outside? I have prepared the house, and have room for the camels."

So I went into the house, and Laban gave me water to wash my feet, and the feet of the men that were with me, and he unharnessed the camels and gave them straw and fodder.

Then they set food before me, but I looked around at the family, and said, "I will not eat until I have told my errand."

"Speak on," they said.

"I am Abraham's steward," I told them. "The Lord has blessed my master greatly; he has given him flocks and herds, and silver and gold, and men servants, and camels and asses. And Sarah, my master's wife, had a son when she was old, and to him he has given all that he possesses."

Then I told what my master had ordered me to do, and of the oath he had made me take before setting out on my errand.

Then I told what had happened at the well on my arrival.

"So I put the ring on Rebekah's forehead, and the bracelets on her hands," I said, "and I bowed my head and worshiped the Lord, who had led me in the right way to find a wife for my master's son. Now if you will deal kindly and truly with my master, tell me: and if not, tell me; that I may know what to do."

"The thing proceeds from the Lord," answered both Bethuel and Laban; "we cannot speak either good or ill. Behold, Rebekah is before you; take her and go, and let her be your master's son's wife, as the Lord has spoken."

All the while Rebekah stood by blushing in confusion, as she listened to this strange and sudden proposal; but she said nothing.

A few hours before, she had never so much as heard of the rich young chief, and now I stood before her as his ambassador and calmly asked permission to carry her off to be his bride.

At the words of the two men, I bowed to the earth, giving thanks to the Lord. Then going to my saddle bags, I brought forth the jewels of silver, and the jewels of gold, and the fine clothing, that Isaac had sent, and gave them to Rebekah. I also gave presents to her mother and to her brother Laban.

This done, my men and I sat down to eat and drink, and we tarried all night.

In the morning I rose up early, and said, "Send me away to my master."

But Rebekah's mother and brother objected, and said, "Let the girl abide with us a few days, at the least, ten; and after that she shall go."

But I was impatient; I was thinking of Isaac, who was anxiously awaiting my return.

"Do not hinder me," I said, "seeing that the Lord has prospered my way; send me away, that I may return to my master."

"We will call the girl, and let her decide for herself," they said.

So they called Rebekah, and asked her, "Will you go with this man?"

"I will go," Rebekah replied.

"Make ready the camels," I ordered my men.

In a very short time Rebekah was ready, and they put her and her nurse and her maidservants upon the camels, and bade her good-by.

"Be the mother of thousands of ten thousands, and may your children possess the gates of them that hate them," they called after her, as we rode away.

Swiftly as the caravan had traveled north, it traveled still more swiftly on the return journey, for was I not bearing home a bride for my beloved young chief? When we halted for the night,

I sang the praises of my master in the willing ears of the maid. How handsome he was—how kind—how brave!

What was Isaac doing all this time? Every evening he wandered pensively in the fields over which he knew the caravan must come, and watched the distant horizon until the darkness shut the line of the sky from his sight.

Then one day which he never forgot, he lifted up his eyes and looked—and there were our camels coming as fast as they could trot.

Isaac ran toward us, and Rebekah lifted her eyes and saw him running, as I halted the caravan.

"What man is this who comes to meet us?" she asked me as I helped her to alight.

"It is my master," I answered.

Rebekah took one glance and dropped her veil over her face.

Isaac saw her face before she did so, and he loved her. It was love at first sight—and always, until death parted them.

Then Isaac took Rebekah by the hand and brought her into his mother's tent, and presented her to his father.

He Did Not Recognize Jacob Because His Hands Were Hairy Like His Brother Esau's

V

THE TWO BROTHERS

"MY dear, how did you ever learn that tale so well?" exclaimed Aunt Maria, as Mary Frances finished telling of the courtship of Isaac and Rebekah, with here and there a word of prompting from her brother. "I am almost tempted to let you two read the next story together; but no—it is a long story, and I think I should tell it to you myself."

So the children settled themselves comfortably, Mary Frances in her rocking chair and Billy on the floor, and the old lady began the story of The Two Brothers.

* * * * * * *

Esau Sells His Birthright

When Abraham died at the age of one hundred seventy-five, he left his wealth to his son Isaac as his birthright. So Isaac became a great chief, the richest in the Land of Promise, and also the head of the Chosen Family.

For a long time Rebekah had no children; and then twins were born, two boys, Esau and Jacob.

Now Esau happened to be the older by a few minutes; and therefore, by right of birth, became his father's heir, for that was the custom of the East.

The two boys were so unlike that no one would ever have guessed that they were twins. Esau was red and freckled; the hair on his body was red, and there was a great mop of red hair on his head. Jacob's body was fair and smooth.

As the boys grew, the difference became more marked. Esau loved to hunt, and spent all his time roaming the plains and hills hunting game with bow and arrow. Jacob was a home boy who loved the tents, and the flocks and herds. Esau was a mighty hunter, Jacob a shepherd.

Well, Isaac loved Esau, who shot the wild deer and brought the choicest bits of venison home to his father; and Rebekah loved the home-staying Jacob, who was always at hand to run her errands and to wait upon her.

Late one afternoon, Esau came in from the chase; he had been out hunting since daylight, and he was ravenously hungry.

Now Jacob was cooking a dish of pottage made of red lentils—a kind of bean growing in that country.

"Give me, I pray you, some of that red pottage, for I am fainting with hunger," Esau cried, trying to reach for it.

"Sell me this day your birthright," said Jacob, drawing back, seeing a chance to make a bargain with his reckless brother.

"See, I am dying of hunger," cried Esau. "What good will my birthright do me?"

"Swear to sell it to me this day," said the wily Jacob.

"I swear; give me the pottage," cried the hungry Esau; and so he sold his birthright to his younger brother.

Then Jacob gave Esau all the bread and pottage he could eat, and Esau ate and drank till he could eat no more, and went away.

Jacob probably excused his meanness by saying to himself, "Oh, well, he despised his birthright, so why shouldn't I take it?"

Soon after this, there was a famine in the land, and Isaac planned to go south to escape it; but the Lord appeared to him, and forbade him.

"Go not down into Egypt," he said. "Sojourn in this land, and I will be with you, and bless you; for to you and to your children I will give all these lands, and I will keep the promise that I made to Abraham your father; and I will multiply your family as the stars of heaven; and in your family shall all the nations of the earth be blessed, because Abraham obeyed my voice, and kept my commandments."

Now that promise and that blessing were a part of Esau's birthright, which he foolishly forfeited. Perhaps he did not know, nor care; but did Jacob know?

To make matters worse, Esau followed the custom of the East, and married two wives from a heathen tribe. This was a great grief to his father and mother, who wished their sons to marry only believers in the one true God.

But even that did not excuse Jacob.

The Stolen Blessing

As Isaac grew older his eyes became dim, so that he was nearly blind, as often happens in the sunny lands of the East.

One day he called his elder son, and said to him, "Esau, my son."

"Here am I," Esau replied.

"See," he said, "I am old, I do not know the day of my death. Now, therefore, take your bow and arrows, and go out into the fields, and hunt me venison, and make me a savory dish, such as I love, and bring it to me, that I may eat, and that my soul may bless you before I die."

Now his father's last blessing was a part of Esau's birthright. Jacob had not told his father what he had done to Esau, but it is likely he had told his mother. Esau, too, kept still, and went off on his hunt.

Now Rebekah heard within the tent what Isaac had said to Esau. Then she did a thing that she must have been sorry for to the day of her death.

She slipped out and found her favorite, Jacob, and whispered to him in great excitement.

"Listen, my son," she said, "I heard your father say to Esau, 'Bring me venison, and make me a savory dish, that I may eat, and bless you before I die.' Now, therefore, my son, do as I tell you. Go to the flock and fetch me two kids of the goats; and I will make a savory dish for your father, such as he loves; and you shall take it to him that he may eat, and bless you before his death."

"But, mother," said Jacob, "Esau is a hairy man, and I am a smooth man. Perhaps my father will touch me. Then I shall seem to him a deceiver, and bring a curse upon myself, instead of a blessing."

"Upon me be the curse, my son," said his mother; "only obey my word, and go fetch the goats."

So Jacob did as he was told, and brought them to his mother; and his mother cooked them and made a savory dish, such as his father loved.

When that was done she took Esau's best clothes, and made Jacob put them on. Then she took the hairy skins of the goats, and fastened them on his arms and hands, and upon the smooth of his neck.

Then she put the dish of meat and the bread that she had prepared into Jacob's hands, and whispered, "Go, my son, and pretend that you are Esau."

Jacob's heart beat fast, and his hands shook so that he almost dropped the dish, as he entered his father's tent.

"My father," he mumbled.

"Here am I. Who are you, my son?" asked the nearly blind old man.

"I am Esau, your first-born," said Jacob; "I have done as you told me. Sit, I pray you, and eat of my venison, that your soul may bless me."

"How is it that you have found it so quickly, my son?" asked Isaac.

"Because the Lord your God sent me good speed," he said, mumbling again.

"Come near, I pray you, that I may feel you, my son, whether you are my very son Esau or not," said the old man.

Jacob went close to his father.

"The voice is Jacob's, but the hands are the hands of Esau," Isaac said in a puzzled tone, as he ran his fingers over Jacob's neck and arms.

He did not recognize Jacob because his hands were hairy like his brother Esau's. But still he was not quite satisfied.

"Are you my very son Esau?" he asked, doubtfully.

"I am," said Jacob.

"Bring the dish near to me," his father said; "and I will eat of my son's venison, that my soul may bless him."

Jacob placed the food before his father and brought him wine.

While all this was going on, Rebekah stood near by, her heart beating so loud that she feared her husband might hear it.

"Come near now, and kiss me, my son," said the old chief, when he had done eating.

Jacob came near, and kissed him. Isaac smelled the smell of Esau's clothing, and blessed Jacob, and said:

"See, the smell of my son
Is as the smell of a field which the Lord has blessed:
And God give you of the dew of heaven,
And of the fatness of the earth,
And plenty of corn and wine:

Let peoples serve you,
And nations bow down to you:
Be lord over your brethren,
And let your mother's sons bow down to you:
Cursed be every one that curses you,
And blessed be every one that blesses you."

As soon as Isaac made an end of blessing Jacob, Jacob seized the dish and slipped out of the tent, followed by his mother. He quickly ran into his mother's tent, threw off Esau's clothing and put on his own. Then he looked out, and there was Esau, swinging across the field from his hunting, a young deer thrown over his shoulder.

Ignorant of what had happened while he was absent, Esau also made savory meat, and carried the dish into his father's tent, where the old chief sat with bowed head, deep in thought.

"Let my father arise, and eat of his son's venison, that his soul may bless me," he cried, in his hearty voice.

"Who are you?" asked the startled old chief.

"I am your son, your first-born, Esau," he replied, in surprise.

Then Isaac trembled exceedingly. "Who then is he that has taken venison, and brought it me, and I have eaten of all before you came, and have blessed him? Yea, and he shall be blessed," he added, in a quavering voice.

When Esau heard these words, he cried with a great and exceeding bitter cry, and the two guilty ones in the neighboring tent heard it.

"Bless me, even me also, O my father," he cried.

"Your brother came with craft, and stole away your blessing," said Isaac in sorrow and anger.

"He is rightly named Jacob, the deceiver, for he has deceived me twice: he took away my birthright, and now he steals my blessing," cried Esau. "Have you not reserved a blessing for me, O my father?"

"See, I have made him lord over you and all his brothers,"

the old chief answered; "and with corn and wine have I sustained him; what then shall I do for you, my son?"

"Have you but one blessing, my father? Bless me, even me also, O my father."

Esau lifted up his voice and wept; and again the two guilty ones in the next tent heard him.

Then Isaac his father answered sorrowfully, and said:

"Behold, away from the fatness of the earth shall be your dwelling,
And away from the dew of heaven from above;
And by the sword shall you live,
And you shall serve your brother;
And it shall come to pass when you shall break loose,
That you shall shake his yoke from off your neck."

With that Esau had to be content.

The Flight of Jacob

Esau had little liking for Jacob even before he stole his father's blessing, and now his dislike turned to hate.

"When my father dies," he said in his heart, "I will kill Jacob."

What he said in his heart, he soon said out loud, as often happens; and his threat came to Rebekah's ears.

She was frightened, as well she might be, for who could foretell what the reckless Esau would do?

"Listen, Jacob," she whispered, "your brother is very angry, and boasts that he will kill you. Now do as I say. Rise up and fly to my brother Laban in Haran; and stay with him a few days, until your brother's anger turns away, and he forgets what you have done to him. Then I will send for you to return home. Why should I lose you both in one day?"

This frightened Jacob, too, so that he was glad enough to go to Haran, or anywhere else, to get away from the angry Esau. His mother dared not tell Isaac of Esau's threat, so she thought of a scheme.

"I am worried," she kept saying to her husband. "If Jacob marries one of these heathen girls, as Esau has done, what good will my life do me?"

Now Isaac was no more pleased with Esau's heathen wives than Rebekah, so he agreed.

"Jacob, you shall not marry a wife of the heathen," he charged him. "Arise, go to your mother's brother Laban in Haran, and take a wife from his family."

Then, little as Jacob deserved it, the good old man gave him his blessing.

Now that he had his father's permission to go, he was anxious to be off. His mother packed his bundle that night, and waking him early the next morning, gave him his breakfast and kissed him good-by.

"Esau will soon forget," she said, "and then you can come home with your new wife."

His mother watched him till he was out of sight; then she went into her tent, and burst into a flood of tears.

"Esau will soon forget," she kept repeating, "and my son will come home."

But Esau did not forget. Jacob did not come home for many a long year, and Rebekah never saw her favorite son again.

On and on he ran, over hill and plain, keeping north toward Haran, looking back from time to time to see if Esau was pursuing. Only his fears pursued him, however.

There he was, a fugitive, all his wealth a bundle of clothes and food, and a staff. He had never before been more than a few miles from home, and now he was setting out afoot on a long journey to a strange country.

As the day wore on, and he saw that Esau was not pursuing, he slowed his pace, but he did not stop. At last, as the sun went down, he came to a lonely spot, a hollow in the hills. Broad sheets of bare rock covered the slopes, and loose stones were scattered over the ground. Here he rested for the night.

The Angels' Ladder

Jacob was alone in a strange country, many miles from his mother's tent. He sat down on a stone and ate his supper hungrily. Then he set the stone for a pillow as comfortably as he could, and lay down to sleep, his staff by his side.

He had never been so tired, and with a homesick longing for his mother, he fell into a sound sleep.

But the weary runaway was not to sleep long, for here in this desolate spot he was to meet with the strangest adventure of his strange life.

As he lay there on the bare ground, he dreamed a wonderful dream. He thought he lay at the foot of a great ladder, a broad staircase that sloped gently up from the earth.

Slowly he gazed up and up, to where the top reached to heaven. He could not move, but just lay there and looked; bright forms were going up and down on it, the angels of God. And, behold, the Lord stood at the top, and a voice came down to Jacob.

"I am the Lord, the God of Abraham, and of Isaac your father: the land whereon you are lying, to you will I give it, and to your children. They shall be as the dust of the earth, and shall spread abroad to the west, and to the east, and to the north, and to the south; and in you and in your children shall all the families of the earth be blessed.

"And, behold, I am with you," the voice went on; "and will keep you wherever you go, and will bring you again into this land; for I will not leave you, until I have done that which I have spoken."

The voice ceased, and the sleeper awoke out of his sleep, and opened his eyes.

"Surely the Lord is in this place," he whispered, "and I did not know it."

Then he shivered, and was afraid; there were the cold stones, and the darkness—nothing more.

"How dreadful this place is!" he said.

Then he remembered the bright vision, and added, "This is none other than the house of God; this is the gate of heaven."

All the rest of that night, Jacob lay tossing on his hard bed, half asleep and half awake.

Early in the morning he arose and looked about him; all was as when he lay down; nothing was changed, but he was no longer afraid.

He looked at the stone that had served as a pillow; he set it up on end like a pillar, and poured a little of the oil his mother had given him on the top of it, and he said, "The name of this place is Beth-el, the house of God."

Then Jacob laid his hand upon the pillar and vowed a vow, which he never afterward forgot.

"If God will be with me, and will keep me in the way that I go, and will give me bread to eat, and clothing to wear, and bring me again to my father's tent in peace, then shall the Lord be my God, and this stone, which I have set up for a pillar, shall be God's house; and of all that he shall give me I will surely give a tenth to him."

Jacob Meets Rachel

This duty being done, Jacob ate his breakfast, and set out on his long journey north with new courage in his heart. Past Da-mas-cus, past the Leb-a-non mountains, on and on he went, toiling slowly on foot, sleeping wherever night overtook him.

He remembered how his mother, as she had often told him, had come riding over this trail on a swift camel to her lover, years before.

After many weary days he reached the land of his mother's people. Then, one afternoon, he came to a well, covered by a great, round stone. Three flocks of sheep lay beside it, waiting to be watered.

"Where are you from?" Jacob asked the shepherds.

"Of Haran are we," they said.

"Do you know Laban, the son of Nahor?" he asked.

"We know him," was the reply.

"Is it well with him?"

"It is well," they said; "and here comes Ra-chel, his daughter, with the sheep."

Jacob looked up, and there was a beautiful girl coming toward the well, just as his mother had done many years before. His father had sent a train of ten camels, laden with costly gifts, to meet Rebekah; their son stood before Rachel, a poor, friendless runaway from home.

Even before Rachel reached him he fell in love with her. Without waiting for the help of the lazy shepherds, he grasped the stone, exerted his great strength, and rolled it from the well's mouth, and helped her water her sheep.

Then, scarcely knowing what he did, he kissed her, and broke into tears; for she was the first of his family that he had seen in his long weary march. Then he told the surprised girl that he was Rebekah's son.

She ran home quickly and told her father the tidings; and Laban came out in haste, embraced him, and brought him into the house.

He told Laban all the news of his mother and father, but he did not tell him the real reason for his leaving home.

"Surely you are my bone and my flesh," cried his uncle in welcome.

There was nothing that Jacob did not know about the care of flocks and herds, and Laban soon found him a very willing helper.

"Even if you are my nephew, why should you serve me for nothing? Tell me, what shall your wages be?" Laban said to him, after a month had passed.

Now Laban had two daughters, Leah, the older, who was not particularly good-looking, and Rachel, the younger, who was very beautiful indeed.

"I will serve you seven years for Rachel," Jacob promptly replied to Laban's question.

"It is better that I give her to you than to another man," said Laban; "stay with me."

Jacob served Laban faithfully seven years for Rachel; but it seemed to him that the seven years were only a few days, so great was his love for her.

"Give me my wife, according to our agreement," said Jacob to Laban at the end of the seventh year.

"Very well," said Laban.

Now Laban was a hard man. With Jacob's skill he was growing rich, and he had no mind to lose his daughter and as good a shepherd as Jacob at the same time.

So what did he do but gather all the men of the place to a great marriage feast. How he got Rachel out of the way, the story does not tell; perhaps he locked her up.

Then he had Leah, who was very fond of Jacob, dress in Rachel's clothes, and put on the thick wedding veil such as brides wear in that country, and he married Leah to the unsuspecting Jacob.

When the happy bridegroom lifted Leah's veil, he saw at a glance what his father-in-law had done, and he was very, very angry and heartbroken.

"What is this that you have done to me?" cried Jacob in his rage. "Did I not serve seven years for Rachel? Why have you cheated me?"

"Not so fast, Jacob, not so fast," said Laban, smoothly. "It is not right in our country to give the younger in marriage before the first-born. Wait a while and I will give you Rachel, and you shall serve me yet seven years more for her."

Now, what was Jacob to do? He loved Rachel, and not Leah; and so he agreed. Thus Laban bound him to seven years more of service.

Perhaps Laban had heard what Jacob had done to Esau—who knows? The story does not tell.

In this way, much against his will, Jacob came to have two wives, a thing that often happened in those rude times.

Whenever Jacob saw a traveler's camel approaching, his heart beat fast, for he hoped it might be a messenger from his mother, saying, "All is well, come home." He knew that with his father's wealth, he could easily buy off the greedy Laban. But no messenger ever came, and he knew that Esau was still to be feared.

Jacob Grows Rich

The second seven years passed by, and Jacob said to Laban, "Send me away, with my wives and my children, that I may go to my own country."

All Jacob had to show for his fourteen years of hard service were two wives and a large family.

"Stay with me a while longer," said Laban, "for I see that the Lord has prospered me for your sake. Name your wages, and I will pay them."

"You know how I have served you, and how the flocks and herds have increased under my care," said Jacob.

"Name your price," said Laban.

"You shall give me nothing," replied Jacob. "If you will do one thing for me, I will again feed your flock and keep it. We will divide the goats into two herds, all the speckled and spotted goats into one herd, and all the goats of one color into another herd, and all the speckled and spotted goats shall be my hire. We will also divide the sheep into two flocks, white and black, and the black shall be my hire."

Now the speckled and spotted goats were very few in Laban's herd, and the black sheep were still fewer, so Laban was pleased.

"Certainly," he agreed; "it shall be according to your word."

The same day they sorted them out, and the shepherds drove Jacob's little herd of speckled and spotted goats, and his little flock of black sheep off into the country three days' journey to keep them separate from Laban's. And Jacob continued to keep Laban's flocks as before.

Now Jacob was a very great cattle breeder, even greater than his grandfather Abraham, and his father Isaac, who were the two greatest cattle breeders in all the land of the East.

So it came to pass, that every year when they sorted out Laban's droves, almost all the lambs were black, and almost all the kids of the goats were speckled and spotted, and belonged to Jacob. But when they sorted out Jacob's droves there were very few white lambs, or plain kids for Laban.

Year by year Jacob grew richer and richer, and was able to buy camels and asses, and to hire many servants. At the end of the sixth year Jacob was a very rich man.

No matter what Laban or his sons did, the result was the same; the flocks bred black sheep, and the herds, speckled and spotted goats.

"This man Jacob is taking away all that belongs to our father," Jacob heard Laban's sons saying; "he is getting all our sheep and goats."

Laban, too, gave Jacob black looks, for he did not understand it.

One day the Lord appeared to Jacob, and said, "Return to the land of your fathers, and I will be with you."

This was good news to Jacob, for he longed to return home.

About this time Laban went off to a distant flock to shear his sheep. Then Jacob quietly took Rachel and Leah, with the children, out to visit his own flocks which were pastured three days' journey from Laban's, and there he told them all about it.

Both Rachel and Leah answered, "Is there any portion for us in our father's house? Are we not counted as strangers? Has he not sold us to you, and also quite devoured our money? What do we owe him? All the riches that God has taken away from our father, are they not ours, and our children's? Do what God has told you."

This was enough for Jacob. The time had come to escape from his hard taskmaster.

He placed his wives and children upon the camels. There were eleven boys. Reuben was the oldest, and a little fellow named Joseph was the youngest. Then he gathered his great droves of camels, and sheep and goats and all his wealth, that he had gotten in Haran, and set out for his old home in the Promised Land.

When Rachel was leaving her father's house for the last time, she stole his household gods, images which he then worshiped, and carried them with her, but she said nothing to her husband.

Jacob Escapes from Laban

While Laban was quietly shearing his sheep, Jacob was fleeing by forced marches as fast as he could go. He wanted to put as many miles between himself and Laban as possible.

He passed over the Eu-phra-tes River, crossed the Syrian desert, and headed south toward the mountains of Gil-e-ad.

It was three days before Laban heard the news. He was very angry, and angrier still when he discovered that his household gods were gone. Calling his men, he pursued with all speed, but Jacob was traveling so fast that it was seven days before he caught up with him.

Jacob's tents were pitched in the mountains of Gilead.

Now in the night God had appeared in a dream to Laban, and had warned him not to harm Jacob; so Laban camped near Jacob, and went to see him.

"Why have you stolen away unawares from me, and carried away my daughters as captives of the sword?" he demanded. "Why did you fly secretly, and not tell me, that I might have sent you away with mirth and with songs, and kissed my daughters and their children good-by? Now you have done a foolish thing. It is in my power to do you hurt. But the God of your fathers warned me not to harm you. Now, even if you must needs be gone, why have you stolen my gods?"

"Because I was afraid that you would take your daughters from me by force," Jacob replied. "Search for your gods; whoever stole them shall not live."

Laban searched through all the tents, and did not find them. Now Rachel had hidden them in her camel's load, and when her father came, she sat upon them. So Laban searched all over the tent, but did not find them.

Then Jacob was angry, and upbraided Laban.

"What is my trespass?" Jacob demanded. "What is my sin, that you have hotly pursued me? Why have you searched through all my goods? What have you found? Bring it out, and let our men judge between us.

"These twenty years have I been with you, and kept your flocks. If any animal was torn by wild beasts, I bore the loss of it, whether stolen by day or by night. These twenty years have I been in your house; I served you fourteen years for your two daughters, and six years for my flock, and you have changed my wages ten times. Except the God of my fathers had been with me, surely now you had sent me away empty handed."

"The daughters are my daughters, and the children are my children, and the flocks are my flocks; all that you see is mine; but what can I do this day to these my daughters or their children? Come now, let us make a covenant, I and you; and let it be for a witness between us," Laban answered.

So Jacob took a stone and set it up for a pillar. "Gather stones," he said to his men; and they took stones and made a great heap; and they all ate together there by the heap.

The name of it was called Miz-pah, meaning watchtower; for Laban said:

"The Lord watch between me and thee,
When we are absent one from another."

"Let this heap, and this pillar be witness that I will not pass over this heap to you," said Laban; "and that you will not pass over this heap and this pillar to me, for harm. The God of our fathers, Abraham and Nahor, judge between us."

To this Jacob swore by the fear of his father Isaac, and they ate bread, and tarried all night in the mountains.

Early in the morning Laban rose up, and kissed his daughters and their children, and blessed them. So Laban departed in peace, and returned to his own country, and Jacob went on his way to his father's tents.

Jacob Sends Gifts to Esau

Jacob's adventures were not yet over; he still had a great danger to face, the meeting with his older brother Esau. Esau was now the chieftain of a fierce and warlike tribe, which lived at Mount Seir, in the country of Edom, far to the south.

Twenty years before, Jacob had stolen his father's blessing, which was Esau's by right of birth, and Esau had threatened to kill him. In fear of his life, Jacob had fled to Laban, his uncle. Now he was returning, a great shepherd prince. What would Esau do?

Jacob sent a message of peace to his brother. "I have sojourned with Laban, and stayed until now," was the message. "I have great flocks and herds, and menservants and maidservants, and I have sent to tell my lord Esau, that I may find favor in his sight."

He had not long to wait before the messengers returned at top speed with startling news.

"We came to your brother Esau, and he is coming to meet you with an armed band of four hundred men."

Jacob was badly frightened; there was no escape, for Esau and his warriors could easily overtake him; he was at their mercy.

Scarcely knowing what he did, he divided his people, and the flocks, herds, and camels, into two companies.

"If Esau attacks one company," he thought, "perhaps the other company may have a chance to escape."

That night Jacob prayed in his tent as he had never prayed before, and this was his prayer:

"O God of Abraham, and of my father, Isaac, O Lord, who said to me, 'Return unto your country, and to your people,' I am not worthy of the least of all your mercies, and of all the truth which you have shewed unto your servant; for with only a staff I crossed the Jordan, and now I have returned with these two companies. Deliver me, I pray thee, from the hand of Esau: for I fear him, lest he come and smite us, the mothers with the children."

The next day Jacob changed his plan. He said to himself, "I will send presents before me to Esau; and afterwards, when I meet him face to face, perhaps he will be the more willing to forgive the wrong I did him."

So he chose a princely gift from his great flocks and herds, five hundred and eighty of the finest animals, and divided them into five droves on the banks of the Jab-bok, a small stream by which they were encamped.

The first drove was made up of two hundred and twenty goats. These he placed in charge of a trusted servant, with this command, "When Esau my brother meets you, and asks, 'Whose herd is this, and where are you going?' you will reply, 'These are your servant Jacob's; it is a present sent to my lord Esau; and behold, he also is behind us.' "

Then he ordered the servant to take the goats across the ford of the river, and go to meet Esau.

The second drove was made up of two hundred and twenty sheep. These he sent across the ford with orders to follow a mile or two behind the first, with the same message to Esau.

Sixty camels, thirty mothers with their thirty colts, formed the third drove; they were sent after the second, with the same message.

The fourth drove was fifty head of cattle, forty cows and ten bulls. They followed the third across, with the same message.

The fifth drove was made up of twenty asses, and ten colts, with the same message.

So that day the five presents passed over the ford, keeping a mile or two between them, and were driven toward Esau.

Before Esau reached Jacob's family he would receive the five presents, and their five messages, one after the other.

It was nightfall before the last gift was safely on its way, and what was left of the two companies retired for the night, to await what would happen.

Jacob Wrestles with an Angel

But Jacob could not sleep. He knew that Esau and his band must be near, and that the morrow must decide his fate. He rose up in the night, and in the darkness moved his family across the ford.

After that he was left alone on the banks of the stream. There a strange and nameless dread of the future came upon him. Before another sunset either he would be slain and his wives and children would be captives, or else Esau would have forgiven him.

Then came the most fearful event of his life. In the darkness a mysterious being attacked him. Jacob was a strong man, and no coward, although a man of peace, and he grappled with his assailant.

They wrestled to and fro all night long, neither uttering a word, grim, silent, and fierce in the darkness. So they wrestled almost till daybreak, and neither could get the better of the other. At last his opponent wrenched the great sinew in the hollow of Jacob's thigh, and lamed him so that he cried in pain.

"Now," said he, "let me go, for the day is breaking."

By this time Jacob knew that it was no human antagonist who wrestled with him, but he held him in a grip of strength. "I will not let you go, except you bless me," he said.

was the brother of Joseph, and the youngest of Jacob's twelve sons.

There, mourning greatly, Jacob buried Rachel and set up a pillar over her grave.

A short time after this, Jacob, with his family and all his possessions, reached his father's tents at Hebron. Rebekah was dead. Isaac, a lonely old man, was very happy to see his lost son, and to know that the brothers were friends again before he died.

Death came to him at the age of one hundred and eighty, and Esau and Jacob buried him with his wife and his father and mother in the cave of Machpelah.

When their father's wealth was divided between the two brothers, they were so rich in cattle that there was not land enough for both; so Jacob remained in Canaan, which was the Promised Land; and Esau went back to Mount Seir.

Jacob became the head of the Chosen Family, who many years afterwards were known as the Children of Israel; and Esau, the prince of a great heathen people in Edom.

* * * * * * *

As their Aunt ceased speaking, the children sat silent for a moment, and then Billy spoke up from his place on the floor:

"Why, Aunty, those stories are great."

"Yes," added his sister, "I felt as though I really knew the family. I seemed to travel along with them from place to place—and I imagined I could hear them talking."

Her aunt nodded her head. "Just so, my child, just so. That is the feeling that all people have who study the Bible. Not only do they make friends of the Bible People, but they learn to know God himself as a friend."

"Yes, indeed; I see that," said the little girl. "How near a friend he was to those people. When you spoke of Joseph, I remembered that God helped him, too."

At the mention of Joseph the boy sat upright.

"I am very glad," said her aunt, "for that is the next story."

JOSEPH BUILT GREAT STOREHOUSES TO STORE THE GRAIN

VI

THE STORY OF JOSEPH

WHEN the two children opened Uncle Ben's book the next day, you can imagine how happy they were to find the story in Joseph's own words, just as he might have told it to his children. Without waste of time Billy seized the book and plunged into the story, while his sister sat eagerly listening.

Sold Into Slavery

My father, Jacob, loved my mother, Rachel, very dearly. Soon after she died he moved his family and all his cattle into the Vale of Hebron, and there we pitched our tents.

Baby Benjamin and I were own brothers, the only children of our mother. Now father had twelve sons, so that the other ten were really our half brothers. Because we were the youngest, it was natural that he should love us more than the others, who were grown men, well able to take care of themselves.

While our brothers were tending the flocks and herds, we two boys played about the tents, and became very dear to each other. As I grew older I went into the fields to assist my brothers, and Benjamin was left at home.

These ten brothers were a wild and lawless set, always getting into mischief and making trouble for our father, who was a very rich chief. When I was about seventeen years old, I innocently aroused their ill will by telling father some of their doings, which were worse than usual. Instead of being sorry for what they had done, they turned their anger on me.

About this time father gave me a new coat, a gay tunic of many colors; and of course I was very proud of it, as any boy would be. When the ten saw this coat, they were angrier still, and never after that gave me a civil word.

One thing leads to another, and now came a happening that made them hate me still more. One night, after a busy day binding sheaves of wheat, as we lay sleeping in the harvest field, I dreamed a dream so strange that I told it to my brothers in the morning.

"Listen to my strange dream," I said. "I dreamed that we were all binding sheaves in the field, and my sheaf rose from the ground and stood upright, and your sheaves all gathered round and bowed down to my sheaf."

How they mocked and jeered! "You will reign over us, will you? We'll see!" they cried.

A few nights later, to make matters worse, I dreamed another and a stranger dream. This puzzled me so much that I could not keep it to myself, but must needs tell my father and my brothers.

"Father," I said, "I dreamed and behold, as I dreamed the sun, the moon, and eleven stars gathered round and bowed down to me."

At this, even father rebuked me, and said, "Shall we indeed come and bow down ourselves to the earth before you?"

This dream made my brothers hate me still more, for they half believed in dreams. I could see that father, too, often thought about it, as he stroked his beard. Perhaps he was as much puzzled as I was—he could not have been more so.

Soon after this my brothers went away with the sheep, to pasture them in the fields at Shechem, a place about fifty miles to the north. As the days went by, and no news came from them, father grew very anxious.

"Joseph, I wonder if anything has happened," he would say. At last, when he could wait no longer, he said, "Come now, I will send you to find out."

"Very well, father, I am ready," I replied.

"Go quickly," he said, "and see whether it is well with them, and bring me word again."

Now, if father had had the slightest notion of the hatred and jealousy of his ten sons toward me, he would not have sent me on such an errand; but he did not know, and neither did I. And so, not thinking of danger, I set out afoot, bravely enough, on the fifty-mile journey. Little did we think when we bade each other good-by that many long years would pass before we saw each other again.

After a hard journey I arrived at Shechem, but neither shepherds nor sheep were to be seen. Full of anxiety, I wandered over the fields looking for them, and at last met a man who told me that my brothers had gone to Do-than, a place fifteen miles farther on. Although footsore and weary, I set off for Dothan, and there I found them, as the man had said.

When my brothers caught sight of me running eagerly across the plain, a wicked plot formed itself in their heads, as Reu-ben told me long afterwards.

"Look," they said to one another, "here comes this dreamer. Come now, let us kill him and throw his body into a pit, and we will say that a wild beast has killed him. Then we shall see what will become of his dreams."

"No, let us not take his life," said Reuben, the oldest of the ten. "Shed no blood; throw him into a pit, if you will, but lay no hand upon him."

To this they agreed, and Reuben, who was the best of the lot, went away, for he wanted no part in what they were about to do. He thought to himself, "After the others are gone, I will return and rescue him out of the pit and send him home to his father."

When I came up, ignorant of their plot, my pleasant greeting was met by black looks. Before I knew what was going to happen, or had a chance to run, they seized me roughly, tore off my new coat, and dragged me toward the pit, crying, "Now, dreamer, what will become of your dreams?"

At the mouth of the pit I struggled desperately and begged for mercy, but they were too strong for me. So they threw me in, and down I went. Half stunned and bruised, I lay at the bottom. Fortunately for me, the pit, which was really an old well, was dry. Then I got up and tried to climb out, but the sides were too steep. There my heartless brothers left me to starve and, deaf to my cries, sat down to eat their dinner.

Now Judah, another of the brothers, had as little liking for murder as Reuben, but he knew nothing of Reuben's plans. While they were eating, a long line of camels suddenly appeared above the horizon. It was an Arab caravan carrying spices and precious things down into Egypt, and Judah saw in it a way of escape.

"What good will it do us to kill our brother and conceal his blood?" he asked. "Come, let us sell him to these merchants; let us not kill him, for he is our brother."

This scheme appealed to them, for it offered them a chance to get rid of me without killing me, and to obtain some money at the same time. So they quickly drew me out of the well and sold me for twenty pieces of silver to the Arab merchants who had now come up. I begged them to let me return home, but I might as well have pleaded with a stone. If my brothers did not care, why should the Arabs care? It was their business to buy and sell slaves, as well as spices; so they bound me and carried me off to Egypt.

Soon after the caravan had disappeared, Reuben returned to rescue me. When he saw that I was not in the pit, he tore his clothes and ran crying to his brothers, "The boy is not there; what shall I do? What shall I say to our father?"

This is what they did. To hide one crime they committed another, and a worse. They killed a goat, and dipped my torn coat in the blood. When they reached home, they brought the bloody coat to father, and said, "We found this in the wilderness; know now whether it is your son's coat or not."

"It is my son's coat," he cried; "a wild beast has devoured him; Joseph is without doubt torn in pieces!"

Then he put on mourning and mourned for me many days. His family tried to comfort him, my guilty brothers among them, but he refused to be comforted, and wept, crying, "I will go down to the grave to my son mourning!"

Even Reuben and Judah, who had saved my life, were too cowardly to tell the sorrowing old man that his lost son still lived.

A Slave in Egypt

After many days' journey, over mountain and desert and river, the Arab caravan at last arrived in Egypt and came to Pharaoh's court, where the merchants offered me for sale as a slave. Since leaving home that last morning on my fateful errand, I had suffered much, and my sufferings had turned me from a foolish boy into a man.

"I must keep up a brave heart, and some day I shall win freedom," I thought, as I looked curiously at the strange scenes about me.

Just then Captain Pot-i-phar, an officer of the king's guard,

So They Quickly Drew Joseph Out of the Well, and Sold Him for Twenty Pieces of Silver to the Arab Merchants

happened to be passing. He looked at me as if he liked me, bought me on the spot, and almost before I knew what was happening we were on our way to his house.

I liked my new master and was faithful and zealous in all his work. Though I was far away from my father's tent, God was with me and prospered me in all that I did. When the captain saw that I was honest and to be trusted he made me overseer of his house and put me in charge of his servants and property, and all that he had.

The captain, who was fully occupied with his important military duties, had little time for his own affairs, and was only too happy to intrust them to so trustworthy a slave as I proved to be. His wealth increased under his new overseer's diligence as never before, and he was more than pleased. I, too, was happy at my success, for it seemed to bring me nearer and nearer to the day of freedom.

But such good fortune was not to last. Through no fault of my own I made an enemy, and that enemy was no less a person than the captain's wife. At first she was very friendly with me, but when I would not do wrong to please her, she turned against me, and falsely accused me to her husband. In this she was aided by some of my fellow servants who were jealous of my position as overseer.

Unfortunately, Captain Potiphar believed his wife's lying words, and became very angry at me. He would not believe me, even though I declared my innocence, but put me into the prison where the king's prisoners were kept.

Alas, I was disgraced. All my hopes of freedom were blasted. I, who as a lad had lived in the free outdoors on the plains with the cattle, sleeping in a tent or on the bare ground, now found myself shut in a prison cell. But I did not despair, for God was with me, and gave me favor in the eyes of the keeper of the prison.

The keeper knew who I was, and did not more than half believe the stories told about me. Very soon he committed to me the care of all the prisoners. He left everything to me and gave me full charge.

Long months passed, and still I was not released, but I did not despair. What my hand found to do, I did with all my might. Then one day two new prisoners were brought in—the chief butler and the chief baker of the king of Egypt. These officers had offended the king, who was very angry with them and ordered them to be thrown into the prison, and both men were placed in my charge.

One night the chief butler and the chief baker each dreamed a dream. When I came in to them in the morning they were looking very sad and downcast.

"Why do you look so sad to-day?" I asked.

"We have dreamed a dream," they replied, "and there is no one who can explain it."

"Do not explanations belong to God? Tell me your dreams, I pray you," was my reply.

Then the chief butler told his dream.

"In my dream," he said, "I saw a vine before me; and on the vine were three branches; the branches budded and the blossoms shot forth, and the clusters brought forth ripe grapes, and Pharaoh's wine cup was in my hand. Then I plucked the grapes, and pressed them into the cup, and gave the cup into Pharaoh's hand."

"This is the meaning of your dream," I replied. "The three branches are three days; within three days Pharaoh will release you, and restore you to your office, and you will give the cup into Pharaoh's hand, as you did when you were his butler. But remember me when it shall be well with you. Show kindness, I pray you, and make mention of me to Pharaoh, and bring me out of this place, and try to obtain pardon for me, for indeed I was stolen away out of the land of the Hebrews, and here also I have done nothing that they should put me into this dungeon."

My explanation of his dream made the butler very happy,

and he promised faithfully to remember me when he was released.

When the chief baker saw that the meaning was good, he said to me, "I also was in my dream, and behold, three baskets of white bread were on my head, and in the topmost basket there were all kinds of baked meats for Pharaoh; and the birds ate them out of the basket on my head."

"This is the meaning of it," I said. "The three baskets are three days. In three days Pharaoh will lift up your head from off you, and will hang you on a tree and the birds will eat your flesh."

On his birthday, which came three days later, Pharaoh made a feast for all his servants. He brought the chief butler and the chief baker from prison, and restored the chief butler to his office again, so that he stood beside his table and gave the cup into his hand. But he hanged the chief baker, just as the dream had foretold.

Yet the chief butler did not remember his promise to me, but forgot all about it. Two long years passed slowly by and I was still in prison. Then a strange thing happened.

Pharaoh's Dream

One night, at the end of that time, the king of Egypt dreamed two strange dreams. When the morning came, his mind was troubled. He sent for all the magicians and all the wise men of Egypt, and told them his two dreams, but none of them could explain the dreams.

Then the chief butler, who was standing by, spoke to the king, saying, "I remember my faults this day. Two years ago Pharaoh was angry with his servants, and put both the chief baker and me in prison. One night we both dreamed a dream. Now, there was with us in the prison a young man, a Hebrew, servant to the captain of the guard; and we told him, and he interpreted our dreams. As he interpreted to us, so it was; me the king restored to my office, and the baker he hanged."

Then Pharaoh sent for me, and they brought me hastily out of the dungeon; and I shaved myself, changed my clothes, and stood before Pharaoh.

I was now thirty years old; thirteen years had passed since as a boy of seventeen I had been sold into slavery, and the last of those years I had spent in prison. The prison pallor showed on my face, but my body was still strong and rugged from the years of youth spent in the open air tending my father's flocks. So I faced the king with a calm and resolute countenance. I thought to myself, "At last my chance has come."

"I have dreamed twice, and no one can tell me the meaning of my dreams; I have been told that you can interpret a dream when you hear it," Pharaoh said to me.

"It is not in me; God shall give Pharaoh an answer of peace," I answered.

"This was my dream," said Pharaoh. "I stood upon the brink of the river, and saw seven cows come up out of the river, fat of flesh and good looking, and they fed in a meadow. Right after them came up seven other cows, poor and ill-looking, such as I never saw in all the land of Egypt for leanness; and the lean and ill-looking cows, instead of eating the grass, ate up the seven fat cows; and when they had eaten them, they were as lean as before. So I awoke."

I listened intently, but said nothing, and the king continued:

"And I saw in my dream seven ears of corn spring up upon one stalk, full and good; and then seven ears, withered, thin, and blasted with the east wind, sprang up after them: and the seven thin ears swallowed up the seven good ears. I told the dream to the magicians, but not one of them could tell me what it meant."

As the king ceased speaking, I knew the answer.

"The dream of Pharaoh is one," I said. "God has declared to Pharaoh what he is about to do. The seven good cows are seven years; the seven good ears are seven years: the dream is one. The seven lean and ill-looking cows that came up after them are seven years, and also the seven empty ears, blasted with the east wind; they shall be seven years of famine. What God is about to do he has showed Pharaoh in his dream."

Not a sound was heard in the court as I continued:

"Behold, seven years of great plenty shall come throughout the land of Egypt, and after them there shall be seven years of great famine. All the plenty shall be forgotten, and the famine shall eat up the land; and the plenty shall be consumed by the famine which follows, for it shall be very sore. The dream was doubled because the thing is established by God, and God will shortly bring it to pass."

As I unfolded the dream, the king's eyes never left me.

"Now, therefore," I continued, "let Pharaoh look for a man sensible and wise, and set him over the land of Egypt. Let Pharaoh do this, and let him appoint overseers over the land who shall take up a fifth part of the harvest in the seven plenteous years. Let them gather the good food of these good years to come, and store up wheat for food in the cities, and let them keep it in storehouses against the seven years of famine, that the people may not perish through the famine."

My explanation seemed good in the eyes of the king. The meaning of the dream was clear. He expressed intense pleasure at the sense and wisdom of my words, and so did all the court.

"Can we find such a one as this, a man in whom the spirit of God is?" the king asked his officers.

I stood before this man whose word was life or death, a slave awaiting my dismissal. Then a thing almost too strange to believe happened.

Fixing his eyes on me, Pharaoh said, "Since God has showed you all this, there is no other man so sensible and wise as you. You shall be my governor, and according to your word shall all of my people be ruled; only in the throne will I be greater than you. See, I have set you over all the land of Egypt."

Then the king, who never did things by halves, took off his

signet ring from his hand and put it upon my hand, and clothed me in garments of fine linen, and put a gold chain around my neck.

"I am Pharaoh," he said, "and without you shall no man lift up his hand or his foot in all the land of Egypt."

As next in authority to the king, I was to ride in the second chariot, and when the people saw me coming, they were to cry, "Bow the knee."

So the slave, who yesterday was in a dungeon, became that day the ruler of Egypt, second in power only to the king himself.

Joseph, the Ruler of Egypt

There was no time to be lost. I did not lose a day—no, not a minute, in setting about my work. I divided all Egypt into districts, and appointed an overseer over each district.

Then I rode up and down the country in my chariot and warned the people of the coming danger. I encouraged the farmers to plant their fields, and to grow large crops of wheat and rye and millet and barley. I distributed seeds to those who had none.

I built great storehouses in the cities and in each district to store the grain. When the harvest time came the people gathered all that was not required for their daily needs and brought it into the storehouses.

For seven plenteous years the land brought forth abundant crops, such as had never been heard of, and we gathered up all the grain as the sands of the sea. At first we kept account of the number of bushels, but soon it poured in so fast that we left off counting, for it was countless.

I heard that some laughed and mocked behind my back and said, "Ha! Ha! there will be no famine."

But none ever dared mock to my face, or to withhold his surplus, for Pharaoh approved of all that I did. I had ever before me a picture of the time to come when the people, and even the cattle, would be crying with hunger, and I would open the storehouses and give them food.

Meanwhile I had married, with the king's permission, a girl who was as good as she was beautiful, As-e-nath, the daughter of a priest of On. Before the famine came we had two boys born to us. The first-born I called Ma-nas-seh, and the second I called E-phra-im.

Then the seven years of plenty came to an end; and famine stalked through the land, as I had foretold. The famine spread throughout Egypt and all the neighboring lands; but in Egypt alone there was bread.

When the people were famished with hunger, they cried to Pharaoh for bread.

"Go to Joseph; what he says to you, do," he told them.

When they came, I opened the storehouses and supplied their needs; for the famine was sore in Egypt, and the land would yield nothing. It was no better in the surrounding countries, and their people came down to Egypt and begged me to save their lives, and I supplied them with food.

Joseph's Brothers Go to Egypt

Now the famine was bitter in the land of Canaan, and father Jacob's grandchildren came to his tent door crying for food, as they afterwards told me.

"Why do you stand there looking at one another?" Jacob asked his sons. "I have heard there is food in Egypt. Go down and buy for us, that we may live, and not die."

So my ten half brothers came down into Egypt to buy corn. But father Jacob would not permit my brother Benjamin to go with them.

"I am afraid something might happen to him," he said.

My father believed that I was dead, torn in pieces by wild beasts, and he had never ceased to blame himself for sending me on that errand to my brothers; and all the time my heartless brothers knew the truth, but never told him.

When the ten arrived in Egypt, they came with all the other starving people, and bowed down before me, begging for food.

I saw them in the crowd, and knew them at once, but they did not know me; they saw in me only the food controller of Egypt.

"Where are you from?" I made myself strange to them, and spoke roughly.

"From the land of Canaan to buy food," they replied.

"You are spies, come to spy out the nakedness of the land," I said, still more roughly.

"No, my lord," they replied, "but to buy food are your servants come. We are all one man's sons; we are true men, and not spies."

"No," I said, "you are come to spy out the nakedness of the land."

"We are twelve brothers," they said, "the sons of one man in the land of Canaan; the youngest is at home with our father, and one is dead."

"By the life of Pharaoh, your words shall be proved," I cried; "you shall not leave here until your youngest brother is brought down. Send one of you and let him fetch your brother, that I may know whether there be truth in you, or else by the life of Pharaoh surely you are spies."

So I put them all together in prison for three days. On the third day I had them brought before me again.

"This do, and live," I said to them, "for I fear God. If you are true men, let one of you be bound in prison, but let the others go and carry corn for the famine of your houses, and bring your youngest brother down to me; so shall your words be proved, and you shall not die."

To this they agreed. They said one to another, "We are truly guilty concerning our brother Joseph. When he begged us not to sell him and we saw the distress of his soul, we would not listen."

"Did I not say to you," Reuben answered, "'do not sin against the child', and you would not listen; therefore now, his blood is required."

They did not know that I understood every word, for I talked with them through an interpreter. My heart was touched, and I was so overcome that I went out of the room and wept. When I returned, I chose Sim-e-on as hostage, and bound him before their eyes and sent him back to prison.

Then I sent the nine men to the storehouse, and ordered my steward to fill their sacks with corn, and to put every man's money in his sack, and to give them provision for the journey; and thus he did.

As soon as their beasts were loaded with the sacks of grain, they set out on their journey north, leaving Simeon bound in the prison. When they arrived at their camping place for the night, one of them opened his sack and saw his money.

"My money is restored," he cried; "lo, it has been put back into my sack."

When they saw the bundle of money, they were afraid, and turned trembling one to another saying, "What is this that God has done to us?"

After a long and weary journey they reached home, and told their father, Jacob, what had happened to them—how the ruler of the land had spoken harshly to them, called them spies, bound Simeon in prison, and ordered them to bring Benjamin down to Egypt to prove that they were true men, and not spies.

When they opened the first sack, and found the money they had been too frightened to open the others, but when they did untie them their worst fears were realized—every man's bundle of money was in his sack; and when they and their father saw the money they were afraid.

"You have robbed me of my children," their father cried.

"Joseph is dead, Simeon is in prison, and now you will take Benjamin away. All these things are against me."

"Slay my two sons," Reuben answered, "if I bring him not back. Give Benjamin into my charge, and I will bring him to you again."

"My son shall not go down with you," Jacob replied; "for his brother is dead, and he only is left. If harm befall him by the way in which you go, then shall you bring down my gray hairs with sorrow to the grave."

So he would not let Benjamin go.

The Brothers Go Again

The second year came, and still the parched ground would yield nothing; the famine grew worse and worse.

The corn the brothers had brought from Egypt had soon been eaten up, for there were about sixty mouths to feed in Jacob's family. When the mothers brought their children to their grandfather's tent, crying with hunger, the tender-hearted old man could resist no longer.

"Go down into Egypt again," he said to his sons, "and buy us a little food."

Then Judah, the son who first thought of selling me into slavery, told once more why they could not go.

"Father," he said, "the man warned us solemnly that we should not see his face again unless we brought our youngest brother with us. If you will send Benjamin with us, we will go down and buy food; but if you will not send him, we will not go. The man would arrest us for spies, and put us in prison with Simeon."

"Why were you so foolish as to tell the man you had a brother?" cried Jacob.

"The man asked us strictly about ourselves and our family," replied Judah. "'Is your father living? Have you another brother?' he inquired, and we told him. How could we know that he would say 'Bring your brother down'? Send the lad with me, and we will go, that we may live, and not die, and you, and our little ones. I will be security for him. If I do not bring him back, I will bear the blame for ever."

At last their father yielded; there was nothing else to do.

"If it must be so," he said, "do this; carry down a present to the man, some balm, honey, spices, nuts, and almonds; and take double money with you, besides the money that was returned in your sacks—perhaps it was an oversight. Take also your brother and go, and God Almighty give you mercy before the man, that he may release Simeon and return Benjamin; for if I am robbed of my children, I am robbed indeed."

So the brothers got ready their presents, and took a double supply of money, for they had plenty of gold and silver, but no food, and came down into Egypt, and brought Benjamin with them.

When they arrived they came to me as before, and bowed themselves to the ground. I eyed them with seeming sternness, although when I saw Benjamin my heart yearned over him.

"Bring these men into my house," I said to my steward, "and prepare a feast, for they shall dine with me at noon."

When the steward brought them in, they were afraid, and said to themselves, "He will accuse us of stealing the money that was returned in our sacks, and seize us and hold us as slaves."

They took the steward aside, and told him about the money.

"Peace be to you; fear not," the steward replied, smiling. "The God of your father has given you the treasure in your sacks; I had your money and put it back. To-day you are to dine with the governor."

When they heard this their fears were much relieved, and they wondered what it all meant. Then the steward brought in Simeon from prison, and gave them water to wash their feet.

When I came in at noon, they laid their present before me, and bowed themselves to the earth. I thanked them, speaking in Egyptian, through my interpreter.

"Is your father well, the old man of whom you spoke? Is he still living?" I asked.

"Your servant our father is well; he is yet alive," they replied, bowing low.

Then turning my eyes to Benjamin, my younger brother, I asked, "Is this your youngest brother, of whom you spoke to me?" To him I said, "God be gracious to you, my son."

The tears rose to my eyes as I looked at Benjamin with whom as a boy I had played about our father's tent in far-off Hebron. Turning away quickly, I hurried to my chamber, and wept there. Then I washed my face and returned to my wondering brothers.

"Let the dinner be served," I said to the steward.

I sat alone at a separate table, and they at a table by themselves, for it was then the rule that the Egyptians should not eat bread with the Hebrews. My brothers still supposing me to be an Egyptian, sat before me; the eldest, Reuben, according to his birthright, and the youngest Benjamin, according to his youth, the men wondering how I knew their ages. I sent food to them from my table, but Benjamin's plate held five times as much as his brothers'. So they ate and drank and were merry with me.

When the dinner was over, I gave orders to the steward secretly:

"Fill the men's sacks with food, as much as they can carry, and put every man's money in his sack's mouth as before; and put my silver cup in the sack's mouth of the youngest, with his corn money." And the steward did so.

The next morning at daylight, the eleven brothers set out on their return, with their beasts loaded with as much grain as they could carry.

When they had left the city, but were not yet far off, I said to the steward, "Up, follow after the men, and when you overtake them, say, 'Why have you returned evil for good? Where is my master's silver cup? You have done evil in taking it away.'"

Mounting his chariot, the steward soon overtook the men, and demanded the silver cup.

"Why does my lord say such things?" they cried, in fear. "God forbid that we should do such a thing. Behold, the money that we found in our sacks before, we brought again to you out of the land of Canaan. How then should we steal silver or gold out of your lord's house? Let him with whom the cup is found die, and we also will be my lord's slaves."

"Now let it be according to your words," the steward replied. "He with whom the cup is found shall be our slave; the others shall be blameless."

The steward searched every man's sack, beginning at the eldest. The cup was found in Benjamin's sack. Then the brothers tore their clothes, reloaded their beasts, and returned to the city.

Joseph Makes Himself Known

When Judah and his brothers arrived at my house, I was there waiting, and they fell to the ground before me.

"What deed is this that you have done?" I demanded, sternly. "Did you not know that such a man as I would surely find you out?"

"What shall we answer my lord?" cried Judah. "What shall we say? How shall we clear ourselves? God has found out the wickedness of your servants; behold, we are my lord's slaves, both we, and he also in whose hand the cup is found."

"God forbid that I should do so!" I exclaimed harshly. "The man in whose hand the cup is found, he shall be my slave; but as for the rest of you, you are free to go in peace to your father."

I was putting the ten to the final test. Would they sacrifice Benjamin to save their own skins? Upon their decision depended their fate.

Then Judah came near—Judah, the very man who had sold me into slavery—and said, "Oh, my lord, let your servant, I pray you, speak a word in my lord's ears, and let not your anger burn against us, for you are even as Pharaoh.

"My lord asked his servants, 'Have you a father, or a brother?'

"We said, 'We have a father, an old man, and a child of his old age, a little one; and his brother is dead, and he alone is left of his mother, and his father loves him.'

"And you said, 'Bring him down unto me, that I may set my eyes upon him.'

"And we said unto my lord, 'The lad cannot leave his father; for if he should leave his father, his father would die!'

"And you replied, 'Except your youngest brother come down with you, you shall see my face no more.'

"And it came to pass when we came to our father that we told him the words of my lord.

"Our father said, 'Go again, buy us a little food.'

"'We cannot go down,' we said, 'for we may not see the man's face, except our youngest brother be with us.'

"Our father said to us, 'You know that my wife Rachel gave me two sons; and the one went out from me; and I said, surely he is torn in pieces; and I have not seen him since; and if you take this one from me and mischief befall him, you shall bring down my gray hairs with sorrow to the grave.'

"Now, therefore, when I come to my father, and the lad is not with us, seeing that his life is bound up in the lad's life, it shall come to pass that he will die, and we shall bring down the gray hairs of our father with sorrow to the grave.

"For your servant became security for the lad, saying, 'If I bring him not back, then shall I bear the blame to my father for ever.'

"Now therefore, let me, I pray you, abide instead of the lad, a slave to my lord; and let the lad go up with his brothers. For how shall I go up to my father, if the lad be not with me, lest I see the evil that shall come to my father?"

"Let every Egyptian leave the room," I cried, as Judah finished.

When I was alone with my brothers I broke down and wept

aloud, and could not control myself. The Egyptians heard the sound of my weeping and wondered.

"I am Joseph," I cried to my brothers in their own tongue. "Does my father yet live?"

They could not answer me, for they were troubled to see the ruler of Egypt, whom they feared, weeping and crying, "I am Joseph, your brother."

"Come near to me, I pray you," I cried to them.

"I am Joseph your brother whom you sold into Egypt," I said, the tears running down my face.

"Now be not grieved, nor angry with yourselves, that you sold me, for God sent me before you to preserve life. For these two years the famine has been in the land; and there are yet five years in which there shall be neither plowing nor harvest. And God sent me before you to preserve you a remnant in the earth, and to save you alive by a great deliverance. So now it was not you that sent me here, but God; and he has made me a father to Pharaoh, and lord of all his house, and ruler over all the land of Egypt.

"Make haste, and go up to my father, and say to him, 'Thus says your son Joseph, God has made me lord of all Egypt. Come down, and tarry not. You shall dwell in the land of Go-shen, and you shall be near me, you and your children, and children's children, and your flocks, and your herds, and all that you have; for there are yet five years of famine.'

"Behold, your eyes see, my brothers, and the eyes of my brother Benjamin, that it is my mouth that speaks to you. And you shall tell my father of all my glory in Egypt, and of all that you have seen; and you shall haste and bring him down."

Then I fell upon Benjamin's neck and wept; and Benjamin wept upon my neck; and I kissed my brethren, and forgave them all.

After that, I left off weeping, and we talked to one another freely.

Jacob Moves to Egypt

The good news that my brothers had come soon spread, as good news will. When the king heard it, he was pleased, and all the court with him.

"Tell your brothers to load their beasts," said he to me; "and go up to Canaan and fetch their father and their households and come down to me, and I will give them the fat of the land. Tell them they are to take wagons for their little ones and their wives, and bring their father and come, for the good of the land of Egypt is theirs."

I did so, and gave them provisions for the journey. To each of them I gave a change of clothing; but to Benjamin I gave three hundred pieces of silver, and five changes of clothing. To my father I sent twenty asses loaded with the good things of Egypt.

Then I bade them good-by, and said, "See that you do not fall out by the way."

The journey of the brothers north was not a very happy one, even though they were carrying great supplies of food, for they also carried guilty consciences. They kept asking themselves, "What will our father say when he finds out that we sold Joseph into slavery?"

As they drew near to Hebron they became more uneasy. "Who will tell him?" they asked, looking at one another.

"You must tell him," said Judah to Reuben.

"No," said Reuben to Judah. "You tell him; you proposed to sell Joseph."

At last the journey was over, and the tents of Jacob came in sight. When Jacob saw the string of wagons, and the twenty beasts of burden, perhaps he wondered, "Whom have they been plundering now?"

Benjamin ran to him crying, "Father, father, Joseph is alive; he is governor over all the land of Egypt."

The poor old man sank to the ground and his heart fainted. He could not believe the story—it was too good to be true.

When they gave him my message he looked at the wagons, and his spirit revived. He threw himself on Benjamin's neck and cried, "It is enough; my son Joseph still lives; I will go and see him before I die."

They unloaded their corn and provisions, and showed him all that I had sent, and his suspicions were aroused. The brothers watched him in fear; they knew their time had come.

"Reuben," asked the old man, sternly, "how came Joseph in Egypt?"

Reuben did not reply, but looked at Judah, who hung his head in shame.

"Father, forgive us," he said. "He was not killed by wild beasts; we—we sold him—into slavery."

The truth had come out at last.

The old man looked at them in horror, but said nothing—what could he say?

He bowed his head and tottered into his tent. He saw my torn coat hanging by his bed. For twenty-two years his heartless sons had let him think that I had been devoured by wild beasts—they had let him suffer and had never said a word. The heart-broken old man threw himself on his bed in an agony of grief and wept.

As he lay there his sorrow gave way to anger.

"Joseph, a slave—sold into slavery!" Then his anger gave way to happiness. "Joseph is alive—alive!"

Then he rose up, a new man, and went out to the guilty men.

"Strike the tents!" he ordered. "Pack up our goods; we will go down into Egypt."

This took some time, for Jacob's family now numbered sixty-six, sixty-seven counting himself, men, women and children; besides their flocks and herds and servants. At last the cattle were gathered, the tents were taken down, the women and children placed in the wagons, the beasts loaded; and then the caravan set off on the march south.

As they neared the land of Goshen, which lies in the delta of the river Nile, Judah went on before to notify me that they were coming, and I mounted my chariot and rode to meet my father.

Twenty-two long years had passed since I had seen him, but when I looked at him I forgot that I was governor of Egypt, and put my head on my father's shoulder and wept a good while.

"Now let me die, since I have seen your face, and you are yet alive," cried the good old man.

After that, I took five of my brothers with me, and presented them to Pharaoh.

When they were brought in, Pharaoh asked them, "What is your occupation?"

"Your servants have been keepers of cattle from our youth up even until now, both we, and our fathers," they replied. "To sojourn in the land are we come; for there is no pasture for our flocks in the land of Canaan. Now, therefore, we pray you let your servants dwell in the land of Goshen."

"Your father and brothers are come to you; the land of Egypt is before you," the king said to me. "Let them dwell in the best of the land, in the land of Goshen; and if you know any able men among them, make them overseers of my cattle."

Then I brought in my father, and set him before Pharaoh.

"How old are you?" Pharaoh asked him, kindly.

"The days of the years of my life are one hundred and thirty years," said father Jacob, and lifting his hands he asked God's blessing on the king for all his kindness.

So the Children of Israel, as Jacob's family was called, dwelt in the land of Egypt, in Goshen; and they grew rich in possessions, and greatly multiplied in numbers.

The Children of Israel in Egypt

Before our father died at the age of one hundred and forty-seven, after having been in Egypt seventeen years, he called us to his bedside and gave us his last commands.

"I am to be gathered to my people," he said; "bury me with my fathers in the cave of Machpelah in the land of Canaan, with Abraham and Isaac."

This we promised, and he gave us his blessing, and foretold what was to come.

"Behold, I die," he said; "but God will be with you and bring you again to the land of your fathers. Each one of you will become a tribe, and there will be twelve tribes of Israel; and after many years God will lead your children up to possess the land of Canaan according to his promise."

With many other words also our father charged us, and when he had made an end, he gathered up his feet into the bed, and yielded up his spirit.

After our weeping was over, I ordered the physicians to prepare him for burial, and they did so.

When seventy days of mourning had passed, I went to Pharaoh.

"My father made me swear to bury him in the land of Canaan," I said. "Now therefore, let me go up, I pray you, and bury my father, and I will come again."

"Go up and bury him as he made you swear," the king answered.

So we went up, my brothers, and all the chief men of Egypt, with chariots and horsemen, a very great company, and buried our father in the cave of Machpelah in the land of Canaan.

Now when my brothers saw that their father was dead, their consciences troubled them again.

"It may be that Joseph will hate us, and will fully repay all the evil which we did to him," they said to one another.

"Before he died, our father commanded us to ask your forgiveness," they came to me and said. "Now therefore, forgive, we pray you, this wrong your brothers did you."

Then they fell down before me and said, "Behold, we are your servants." When they spoke thus, I wept.

"Do not fear," I said. "Am I in the place of God? As for you, you meant evil against me, but God meant it for good, that many people might be saved alive. Do not fear; I will protect you and your little ones."

At last they felt that they were truly forgiven, but they never ceased to be sorry.

* * * * * * *

The story ended; the Oriental figures in their flowing robes seemed far away, and with a long-drawn sigh the children closed the book and hurried to find Aunt Maria. "We know all about Joseph," both exclaimed.

"And that's as far as we know," Mary Frances finished, when they had retold the story.

"Aunty, how did the Children of Israel get out of Egypt?" asked Billy.

"That is a splendid question," said his aunt. "Would you like me to tell you about it? It's a famous story."

"Would we?" he replied eagerly.

"Well, then—to-morrow."

So the next evening Aunt Maria began the story of The Chosen People in Slavery.

THE CHOSEN PEOPLE IN SLAVERY.

THE CHOSEN PEOPLE IN SLAVERY

"I am the LORD thy God, which have brought thee out of the land of Egypt, out of the house of bondage. Thou shalt have no other gods before me."—EXODUS 20: 2, 3.

THEN MOSES BURIED THE DEAD MAN IN THE SAND

VII

A GREAT LEADER

The People are Oppressed

WHILE the good Pharaoh whom Joseph served was alive, the Chosen People were well treated. When he and Joseph were dead and forgotten, the Egyptians began to oppress them.

The wicked Pharaoh who was now king had forgotten all that Joseph had done for the Egyptians, or it may be, had never even heard of him.

"See, these people have become mightier than we; perhaps when war comes they will take sides with our enemies. Let us keep them down," he said to his officers.

So the Egyptians set taskmasters over the Hebrews, and made them slaves. They carried their burdens, made bricks and mortar, built their cities, and toiled in the fields. Their masters drove them to work with whips, and cared nothing for their lives.

But still they grew and increased. Their lives were bitter and their service hard, but the Egyptians could not keep down their numbers.

Then this wicked king formed a cruel plan.

"Every son that is born to the Hebrews you shall throw into the river Nile, and every daughter you shall save alive," was the order given.

He would destroy them by killing every male child. The officers of Pharaoh were to search them out as fast as they were born and hurl them into the river. Thus the boys were sentenced to death even before they came into the world.

The twelve sons of Jacob and their children had grown into twelve tribes, numbering probably two million people. God had promised Jacob that the Chosen People should be led back to the Promised Land, from which he had fled to escape the famine.

This promise was now about to be kept, and Moses was chosen for the great task of setting his people free.

Moses is Born

When this oppression was at its height, Moses was born in the tribe of Levi. His mother had two other children, Miriam and Aaron, who were born before the cruel law had gone into effect.

Moses was a beautiful child, but he gave his mother no joy, for she knew that he was sentenced to die. One day the officers would find him—and then a horrible death.

She hid him three months; and then one day she saw the officers searching about, and knew that she could not conceal him much longer. At her wits' end, she thought of a plan to give her baby a chance for his life.

"I will put him in the river myself," she said. "It may be that God will send some kind-hearted Egyptian to find him, who will have pity and spare his life."